A Chanticleer Press Edition

BIRDS
OF
NORTH
AMERICA

AUSTIN L. RAND

leday & Company, Inc., New York

ANIMAL LIFE OF NORTH AMERICA SERIES

Birds of North America
by Austin L. Rand

Fishes of North America
by Earl S. Herald

Insects of North America
by Alexander and Elsie Klots

Invertebrates of North America
by Lorus and Margery Milne

Mammals of North America
by Robert T. Orr

Reptiles and Amphibians of North America
by Alan Leviton

Half-title page photograph: Barn owls
Title page photograph: California gulls

All rights reserved under International and
Pan-American Copyright Conventions.

Published in the United States by Doubleday &
Company, Inc., New York. Distributed in Canada
by Doubleday Canada Limited, Toronto.

Planned and produced by Chanticleer Press, Inc., New York.

Manufactured by Amilcare Pizzi, S.p.A., Milan, Italy.

Library of Congress Catalog Card Number 75-147-352.

CONTENTS

Preface

When as a youth in Nova Scotia I became aware of birds, the local "bird man" impressed on me the importance of learning firsthand what each bird did, and how and where it lived, as well as what it looked like. When I got my first assignment as a professional ornithologist, to spend two years with an expedition in Madagascar, I turned to an old Africa-hand for advice. He pointed out that all birds would be new to me, but I should not on that account try to record everything I saw birds do each hour. Rather I should observe them day after day until finally I could summarize in a paragraph the normal behavior of a species, its way of life in its usual haunts, and something of its temperament.

This advice has served me well, not only in field work in Madagascar, New Guinea, the Philippines and El Salvador, but also in America where I have observed birds from ocean to ocean and from Florida to Alaska. Birds have been an avocation as well as a vocation, and the pleasure and stimulus of seeing them and writing about them has been a lodestar of my being.

Most of the impressions of birds recorded in the following pages can be traced to the spot where a certain incident occurred. The magpies awakened me by walking and chattering on the galvanized iron roof when I slept at the ranger station in the Cypress Hills, a pine-covered "island" in the Canadian prairies. I saw the roseate spoonbills going to roost with the sunset turning their pink wings to flame while my wife and I were tossing bread to laughing gulls and watching a reddish egret feeding on an islet off the southwest Florida coast. The Canada jays that gave me a ghostly escort appeared in a muskeg spruce forest after I had had an encounter with a black bear in the southern Yukon.

Many of my observations were made evenings and on weekends within a few miles of our house in a town near Chicago. A favorite observation place was a little marshy pond where I watched the gallinule getting its young to bed, the chicken-turned-duck antics of the coot, and the transition from the daytime to the night-time feeding shift of common egrets and night herons. Even the view from our living-room window overlooking a bird-feeding station has yielded such prizes as redpolls, purple finches, evening grosbeaks, redbreasted nuthatches and red-bellied woodpeckers

7

as well as the dozen or so regular customers. This view is more interesting to me than any show on television.

In the following pages the families are arranged in the sequence of the *Checklist of North American Birds*, fifth edition, published by the American Ornithologists' Union in 1957, and that list is also followed for names, both scientific and vernacular. However, the sequence of species within each family has been changed to suit the needs of this volume.

A. L. RAND
CHICAGO, ILLINOIS

Introduction

This book is a survey in pictures and text of the 600 or so birds of regular occurrence in the United States and Canada. But first, a brief resumé of the bird, its place in evolution and in its environment, is in order.

Birds are vertebrate flying animals clad in feathers. Their closest relatives are the hairy mammals and the scaly reptiles. All three trace their ancestry back through geological time to the Jurassic Era. Sharing the general vertebrate pattern of bone, muscle and other organ systems, birds have evolved adaptations for their special way of life. Birds as a group are very active, with good vision, hearing and voice, and quick responses. Their forelimbs are modified into wings for flying but their legs still function for walking, hopping or swimming. The jaws are elongated into a horn-covered, toothless beak for manipulating food and nest material.

The adaptations for flying include a short, stout body, concentrating weight centrally. The bones are light, slender and hollow, with many elements fused for rigidity. The keeled breastbone has the great breast muscles that power flight, while the hip bones are fused into a single unit and the thigh muscles are large for powering the bipedal locomotion.

The feathers are important in several ways. The row of quills on the rear edge of the wing provides a light flexible wing area for flight, and the long tail quills attached to the stumpy tip of the spine act as a rudder. The coat of feathers gives the bird's contours the streamlining so important for flight. The feathers are also good insulators, aiding the bird in maintaining its uniformly high body temperature, irrespective of external conditions. This insulation is also important for the bird's continuous high metabolism and activity, a condition that also depends on its four-chambered heart, which is like that of mammals but unlike that of reptiles.

Usually the feather coat is replaced once a year by moult, but this is gradual so that the bird is never naked and does not lose the power of flight. The ducks, however, are an exception in that they become flightless during one of their two moults.

Plumage coloration of birds is exceedingly diverse. Some species are plain, others patterned; some are conspicuously colored, others cryptically colored. When the sexes are different the male is usually brighter and then the young are like the female.

9

Birds use their voices for various purposes. A crow caws an alarm, a wren scolds a cat, and the members of a winter band of foraging chickadees keep in touch with each other by little calls. But bird song, one of the most arresting and attractive features of birds, has a special role. It is usually sung only by the male in the early part of the breeding season and helps in establishing a territory and in getting a mate. Display is also used. Some birds are monogamous, whereas others are polygamous; the latter tend to depend more on display than song.

The clutch of eggs, varying from one to a dozen or so, is laid in a nest which typically is cup- or basin-shaped and is placed in a wide variety of locations, ranging from the ground up to a hole in a tree trunk or a high branch. Some birds make simple nests; others elaborate ones. The eggs are hard shelled, white or various shades, and with or without markings, and contain much food for the developing embryo. The young of many birds, such as robins and hawks, hatch in a helpless condition, called altricial, and must be brooded and fed in the nest for days or weeks until they are grown. The young of some birds, such as quail and ducks, are clad in down at hatching and, as soon as they are dry, follow the parent.

Over much of North America, migration is one of the conspicuous features of bird life. With the approach of winter, many species move south to a warmer climate, and return north again in the spring to their breeding grounds as vegetation begins to grow and insects become abundant.

Birds occur everywhere over the continent and its adjacent waters, but they are not uniformly distributed. In the far northern Arctic barrens of Ellesmereland there are only about two dozen breeding species, besides a few others that have been recorded as strays. In semitropical Florida more than 400 species have been found, of which more than 170 have been recorded as breeding. The others are winter visitors from the north or are transients on their way summer and winter ranges.

Within each species range the bird lives only in certain habitats—water, shore, marsh, grassland, brushland or forest—and each species has favorite foods. Adaptations to certain foods and habitats are often characteristic of a whole family of birds, or of several unrelated groups. Common song birds of gardens have generalized feet, wings and tail for hopping or walking and flying, and a bill that may be slender for eating insects or thick for cracking seeds, or some intermediate size for a varied diet of insects, fruit and seeds.

Web feet for swimming is characteristic of ducks, pelicans and loons, whereas such birds as herons and ibis have long legs for wading. Swallows and swifts, whose very short legs are suitable only for perching, compensate with long wings and special powers of flight. The hooked bill and claws of owls and hawks are adapted to seizing and tearing large animal prey; the stout, pointed bill of the heron and kingfisher is useful for spearing fishes. But many birds can change their sources of food; they can eat insects in summer, fruit in autumn, and seeds in winter.

Birds, like mammals, are consumers of other animals such as insects, worms, and mice, and plants whose energy ultimately comes from the sun. They have evolved to live in many habitats in many ways. Their song, daytime activity, pleasing colors and interesting behavior, and their diversity have made them one of the most popular groups of animals.

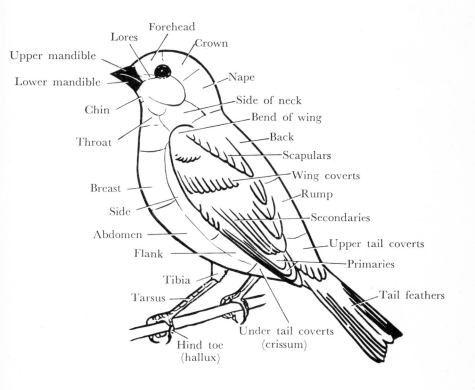

Loons (*Family Gaviidae*)

The wild loud laughter of the common loon (*Gavia immer*) is a hallmark of the northern wilderness. The loon itself, a big swimming bird with a stout dagger-like bill and a stubby tail, is likely to be sitting far out on a clearwater lake. It dives and swims underwater, propelled by large webbed feet so far back on its body that it can only shuffle on land. Its food of fish is caught underwater. Its nest, a sodden heap of vegetation, is built so near the water's edge that the bird hardly needs to come ashore. Two olive-brown, spotted eggs are laid and the downy young swim away with their parents.

When winter comes and the lakes freeze, the common loons migrate seaward and southward. Their long, narrow wings drive them along in swift, strong flight. The winter is spent in coastal salt waters. Then they may assemble in loose flocks of scores of birds.

The common loon is the most southern species and the one most Americans are likely to see, for it nests on islands in lakes of the spruce forest zone across the continent and winters off both our coasts. The loon is about 32 inches long; in summer, the head is all black with a straight black bill; in winter, it is gray-black above, white below, with a pale base extending to the mandible.

There are three other loons: the yellow-billed loon (*Gavia adamsii*), the arctic loon (*Gavia arctica*) and the red-throated loon (*Gavia stellata*). The yellow-billed loon can be seen on its breeding grounds only on the arctic barrens of Alaska or northwestern Canada. In winter, however, it is recognizable by its yellow, slightly upturned bill. The arctic loon, another bird of the lakes of the arctic northwest, winters along our Pacific coast. It is small, measuring about 26 inches long. In summer the crown and hind neck are gray, the throat black; in winter it is much like the common loon but smaller and with a more slender bill. The lakes and ponds of the Arctic and Subarctic are the summer home of the red-throated loon. It winters off both coasts of North America. It is also small, measuring about 25 inches long. In summer it has a red throat patch; in winter it is much like the winter arctic loon but with a more uptilted bill and somewhat grayer upperparts.

Common loon (Gavia immer)

Pied-billed grebe (Podilymbus podiceps)

Grebes *(Family Podicipedidae)*

Nesting grebes are likely to be found on any suitable marshy pond or lake from Florida to Alaska. Grebes float, ducklike, but the bill is pointed and there are no evident tail feathers. Alarmed, a grebe may dive and swim away underwater rather than fly, and it is underwater that it finds its food of small water animals, fish, frogs, insects, and such. In addition to waterproof plumage, the grebe's adaptations to an aquatic life include lobed instead of webbed toes and feet far to the rear of its body. This of course makes walking very difficult and its nest is built, like a raft or an island, of vegetable material among the reeds. The four to seven eggs are whitish at first but the parent covers them when leaving the nest, and they acquire a brownish stain. The young of all but the western grebe are brownish black with a conspicuous pattern of buffy streaks. The young soon swim after the parents, or they may ride on the parent's back, nestling among the feathers. When the young are grown and winter approaches, the northern birds move to coastal salt water or southward into ice-free ponds or lakes.

Breeding across the continent, the pied-billed grebe (*Podilymbus podiceps*) is the only grebe breeding east of the prairies. It favors ponds with much aquatic vegetation in which the bird sometimes skulks; at others it is much in the open, and its loud sonorous call "Cow-cow—" is a characteristic sound of the marshes. When its feathers are fluffed out the pied-bill appears to be a plump bird, but when the feathers are slicked down it appears slender, and then the bird may sink down and swim with only its head and neck exposed. It is a permanent resident in the southern states but there is also an influx of northern birds in winter.

The pied-billed grebe is 13 inches long, generally brownish with a black bar across its rather thick bill. A related species, the least grebe (*Podiceps dominicus*) of Mexico, only 9 inches long, ranges as far north as southeastern Texas.

On large lakes fringed with rushes or tulles, from Manitoba to northern California, the colonies of the large black-and-white western grebe (*Aechmophorus occidentalis*) may contain hundreds or even thousands of closely spaced nests; the wintering flocks on the Pacific coast inlets may be equally large. Equally remarkable are the courtship displays. In one display called the "race," two birds rise upright, side by side, with wings partly spread, and patter across the surface. In another, called the "dance," two birds, each with a mass of water weed in its bill, rise upright, breast to breast, treading water as high as they can. This is our largest grebe, 21 inches long, with a long slender neck; it is black above and white below, in both summer and winter.

There are three other grebes, from 13 to 19 inches long, nesting in ponds, lakes and sloughs of the prairies in the West and Northwest, where they have distinctive head markings. In winter many migrate southward and seaward to winter on saltwater. By that time they have lost the ornamental head plumes and markings and are much alike, blackish above, whitish-tinged-gray below. The smallest species, the eared grebe (*Podiceps caspicus*) is 13 inches long with black head and neck and large orange ear tufts in breeding dress. It nests in dense colonies and winters on the Pacific coast. The horned grebe (*Podiceps auritus*), 14 inches long, has a red neck and a black head with orange-red ear tufts. It is a solitary nester and winters on both coasts. The larger red-necked grebe (*Podiceps grisegena*), 19 inches long, has a red neck and white chin and sides of the face. It also winters on both the Atlantic and the Pacific coasts.

Albatrosses (*Family Diomedeidae*)

To find albatrosses one must go to sea. The best place are of course the far southern oceans where live most of the fourteen species, including the giant wandering albatross which is some 4½ feet long and has a wingspread of nearly 12 feet. All albatrosses are large birds and have long, narrow wings, a bill that has nostrils opening in a pair of tubes at the base and a hook at the tip.

Three species of albatrosses nest on subtropical islands in the western Pacific and, when free of nest duties, live at sea all the way from the offshore American waters westward to Japan. It was these, known as "goony birds," that hindered airplane operation at Midway Island by cluttering the runways and colliding with the planes. The leveling of sand dunes near the runways, which eliminated updrafts of deflected wind for the birds to ride, proved to be a partial solution; the birds no longer congregated there.

In soaring flight, down into the troughs and over the crests of the waves, the black-footed albatross (*Diomedea nigripes*) searches the ocean for squid, crustaceans and fish. These birds also follow ships at sea, gliding like great dark gulls, and when garbage is thrown from the galley the albatrosses swoop down, alight and eat the meat, bread and pastry—in fact, anything but raw fruit.

Since the black-footed albatross sometimes does not breed until it is nine years old, the hundred thousand or so adults that gather each year to nest on Midway, Laysan and other islets far to the west of Hawaii are only a fraction of the whole population. The breeding birds arrive in October and November, form colonies on windswept beaches, display, and scrape shallow nests. Each pair incubates its single white egg for two months. The chick takes six months to grow up and fly away to sea. The black-footed albatross is 52 inches long and its plumage is mostly brownish black.

The Laysan albatross (*Diomedea immutabilis*), ranging over the trackless north Pacific, has a remarkable ability to find its way to its nesting islets west of Hawaii. When a banded bird was taken from its nest on Midway and released on Puget Sound, it later returned the 3200 miles to its nest in ten days. This albatross is a shyer bird than the black-footed albatross, less given to following ships and, on migration, stays farther offshore. The adult is 32 inches long and white with black wings and back.

Top: Black-footed albatross (Diomedea nigripes),
in immature and mature dress
Bottom: A black-footed albatross with her single egg

The short-tailed albatross (*Diomedea albatrus*) is a star-crossed species. In pre-Columbian times it was the commonest albatross on our inshore Pacific waters, judging by the abundance of its bones in west coast Indian middens. When the feather trade flourished, hunters decimated it on its breeding grounds on the islands between Japan and Hawaii. Finally in 1939 and 1941 volcanic activity destroyed its main breeding places. A few survive, but recent records of it are rare, and it is on the international list of rare and endangered species. It is about 28 inches long, and mostly white in color.

There are three other species of albatrosses of far southern waters that have straggled to our coasts, the yellow-nosed albatross (*Diomedea chloro rhynchos*) and the black-browed albatross (*Diomedea melanophris*) coming to our East Coast and the white-capped albatross (*Diomedea cauta*) to our West Coast.

Fulmar, Shearwaters and Petrels

(*Family Procellariidae*)

Shearwaters can be recognized from afar by their rapid gliding flight low over the waves. The open sea is their home and they come to land only to nest; even then they go no farther inland than necessary and form dense colonies on remote islands or sea-facing cliffs. Some nest in burrows, other in crevices in rocks or on rock ledges. A single white egg is laid and both parents care for the young. When the young bird is grown and fat the parents of some species abandon it and it lives on its fat until it finally set out by itself into its watery world.

North America has few nesting birds of this group. The fulmar nests in the Arctic and two other species of shearwaters or petrels nest in the West Indies. But fourteen other species are known to occur in American waters. Some are regular nonbreeding migrants; others are strays far outside their normal range in distant southern oceans.

These shearwaters are medium-sized birds from 12 to 22 inches long and related to the albatrosses, as can be seen by the shape of the bill, wing and feet. Correlated with their smaller size, their gliding flight is more interrupted with wing strokes than is that of the albatrosses.

FULMAR

The fulmar (*Fulmarus glacialis*) is our only shearwater of far northern waters, nesting in great colonies on the ledges of sea-facing cliffs through the Arctic, and in winter ranging from the edge of the sea-ice south over the oceans to waters off New England and California. Almost any animal matter—crustaceans, squids and fish—in the sea is food for the fulmar. Large numbers of these birds follow ships or congregate to feed on the refuse from fishing boats and on scraps from whale carcasses.

In its dark phase the fulmar, about 20 inches long, is generally smoky gray with a yellowish bill; in its light phase it is white with a blue-gray mantle. The latter recalls a large gull, but its flight is shearwater-like, with stiff wing strokes alternating with gliding.

GREATER SHEARWATER

In May and June, the southern hemisphere's autumn, the greater shearwater (*Puffinus gravis*) leaves its nesting grounds on the tiny Tristan da Cunha Islands in the mid-south Atlantic for its north Atlantic wintering grounds. Soon they are found a few miles off the New England coast and on the fishing banks. Their natural food is small squid and fish but the offal from fishing boats is very attractive to them, and milling, screaming swarms may gather to feed on it. Their flight is even more of a glide than that of most shearwaters, although they alight to feed and may even dive. To take off they need a long pattering run. As the northern summer wanes, spring is coming to Tristan and the birds leave the north for their nesting grounds there.

The greater shearwater is about 19 inches long and has the upperparts dark brownish, underparts white, and cap and bill black, contrasting with the white cheeks and throat.

OTHER SHEARWATERS OF REGULAR OCCURRENCE

The Cory's shearwater (*Puffinus diomeda*) visiting our eastern Atlantic waters from August to November, and the pink-footed shearwater (*Puffinus creatopus*) occurring in the eastern Pacific, are very similar to each other and differ from the greater shearwater in the pink bill and paler crown which contrasts less with the white of the throat. The Manx shearwater (*Puffinus puffinus*) visits both Atlantic and Pacific offshore waters and is like the greater shearwater but much smaller, being only 15 inches long.

19

The Audubon's shearwater (*Puffinus lherminieri*) that nests in the Wes Indies and visits our southeastern coastal waters is like the Manx but i still smaller—only 12 inches long. Correlated with its small size it flies witl much flapping and fluttering of wings, gliding less than do the large shearwaters; it alights readily and swims and even dives for the fish tha bulk large in its diet.

There are three species of shearwaters with both upper- and underpart dark. The sooty shearwater (*Puffinus griseus*), while uncommon in th Atlantic, is the most common shearwater off our Pacific coast where a many as 100,000 have been seen in a day, and great flocks sometimes com into bays of the Washington State coast. This species, 18 inches long has the underwing whitish and the bill and feet dark. The slender-billec shearwater (*Puffinus tenuirostris*) is also common off the Pacific coast an sometimes travels with the sooty shearwater from which it differs i having the underwing dark and in being slightly smaller. A third species the pale-footed shearwater (*Puffinus carneipes*), also of the Pacific waters is like the slender-billed but with pale pink feet and bill, and it is large measuring about 20 inches long.

SHEARWATERS AND PETRELS—CASUALS AND STRAYS

The following eight species have strayed to America from their norma ranges to the south: the black-capped petrel (*Pterodroma hasitata*) fron the West Indies; the South Trinidad petrel (*Pterodroma arminjoniana* from the south Atlantic; the scaled petrel (*Pterodroma inexpectata*) and the New Zealand shearwater (*Puffinus bulleri*) from the New Zealand area the Cook's petrel (*Pterodroma cookii*) from the South Pacific; the black tailed shearwater (*Adamastor cinereus*) and the little shearwater (*Puffinu assimilis*) of southern oceans and the Cape petrel (*Daption capensis*) o Antarctic waters.

Storm Petrels (*Family Hydrobatidae*)

Tiny relatives of the giant albatrosses, storm petrels are little larger tha sparrows in body size though their wings are long and rather broad. Thei flight has been called bat-, moth-, or swallow-like as they fly over th water in search of food. Feeding involves a sort of surface dancing, a fluttering of wings in the air and a pattering of feet on the water as the birds snatch up small marine organisms from the surface. Some species follow ships, some species wander widely over the oceans when not breeding, and other species stay near their breeding grounds, which are always on islands.

Storm petrels come ashore only to breed. The nest is in a burrow or crevice; a single white egg is laid and the downy young becomes full-feathered and able to fly before it leaves the nest. Both sexes share nest duties, coming and going only in the dark.

LEACH'S PETREL

Few men know the Leach's petrel (*Oceanodroma leucorhoa*) on land even though they may visit the tiny islands on which the birds have thriving colonies, for during daylight the birds are either in their nest burrows or at sea. Noisy courtship, burrow-digging and change of shifts on the nests occur under cover of darkness when the petrel's chief enemies, the diurnal gulls, are asleep. The birds at sea are active during the day, fluttering and bounding above the waves. Unlike some of their relatives, they may circle ships but do not follow them. This is our most widespread species, nesting on islets off both coasts as far south as New England and California. It is 8 inches long and blackish with a white rump, a grayish wing stripe and a deeply forked tail.

WILSON'S PETREL

While the Leach's petrel is a northern hemisphere bird, the Wilson's petrel (*Oceanites oceanicus*) is a cosmopolitan species nesting on Antarctic islands and migrating to the north Atlantic, the Indian and the central Pacific Oceans. Though reaching our West Coast only as a straggler, the birds are common migrants off our Atlantic coast as far as Newfoundland. They alight on the water, floating as lightly as phalaropes, but in northern waters they are rarely seen doing this. Rather they flit over the water with a dancing or hopping flight and with dangling legs that patter on the surface every now and then.

Obviously immense numbers of these birds are scattered over the northern oceans, an estimate that is reinforced by the reports of Antarctic explorers of acres and acres of these sparrow-sized birds so closely spaced on the water that individuals seem to be touching. The Wilson's petrel,

7 inches long, is like the Leach's petrel but has a whitish wing stripe and a square tail.

OTHER BREEDING STORM PETRELS

The large, 9-inch black petrel (*Loomelania melania*) has a forked tail and is blackish brown except for a grayish wing streak. Though it nests farther south, individuals are found off the California coast at any time of the year. They follow ships and on rare occasions thousands of these birds gather on the surface of the ocean in great rafts. The ashy petrel (*Oceanodroma homochroa*) is similar to the black petrel but is smaller, 7 ½ inches long, and the only pale markings are on the underwing. It nests on California's Santa Barbara Islands and unlike other storm petrels wanders but little. The forktailed petrel (*Oceanodroma furcata*), 8½ inches long, is the most distinctive storm petrel, being pearl gray above and white below. It nests on islets from northern California to Alaska, but is most common in the Aleutian Islands.

STORM PETRELS—CASUALS AND STRAYS

The least petrel (*Halocyptena microsoma*) nests on islets off lower California and wanders north to San Diego. Three other species whose normal ranges are far from our waters have strayed to America: the white-faced petrel (*Pelagodroma marina*), the Harcourt's petrel (*Oceanodroma castro*) and the Galapagos petrel (*Oceanodroma tethys*). Earlier records of the British storm petrel (*Hydrobates pelagicus*) and the black-bellied petrel (*Fregetta tropica*) are not accepted.

Tropic-Birds (*Family Phaethontidae*)

I first saw a tropic-bird as it came from astern on rapidly beating wings mast high, passed and circled the ship as though curious and then went on its way. This was in the West Indies, out of sight of land, and was typical of many sightings. Later, I heard their shrill whistled calls and saw the birds dive headlong, go completely under, pop up, float lightly with tail cocked up and then spring into the air and fly on.

These white, boldly black-patterned sea birds are about 30 to 40 inches

Top: A white pelican (Pelecanus erythrorhynchos) feeding her young by regurgitation. Bottom left: Brown pelican (Pelecanus occidentalis). Bottom right: Gannet (Morus bassanus

long, and their streamer-like central pair of tail feathers makes up mor
than half of their total length. The bill is stout and pointed and all fou
toes on the feet are webbed. Tropical and subtropical seas are the haunt
of the tropic-birds, and marine animals are their food. The single white eg
is laid on bare rock or sand on an island. The downy young is fed at th
nest until it can fly.

Two species with similar habits occur regularly in the southern offshor
waters of North America. The adults of both have red bills and whit
central tail feathers. The red-billed tropic-bird (*Phaethon aethereus*) i
the larger species and has black streaks in its wings and some barring o.
its back. The young, lacking the long tail streamers, is more barred witl
black, and its bill is orange-yellow. The nearest nesting sites are on island
off Mexico's west coast but some individuals come to California offshor
waters. The white-tailed tropic-bird (*Phaethon lepturus*) is the smalle
species and has a solid bar of black near the rear margin of its wings. Th
young have the back barred and the bill yellow. Their nesting sites clos
est to our shores are in Bermuda and the Bahamas and they occur off ou
Atlantic coast north to the Carolinas.

Pelicans *(Family Pelecanidae)*

Pelicans are among our largest water birds and have a most unusual com
bination of characters. The broad bill is a foot or more long and has :
capacious, expandable pouch; the neck is long but is folded in flight; th
wings are long and broad; the body is heavy; tail and legs are short an
the toes webbed. Pelicans fish for a living, using a surprising variety o
methods. They are sociable birds in feeding, at rest, and when nesting. Tw
to four whitish eggs are laid in a crude nest on the ground or in a tre
and the young are fed there on predigested fish. This the young get b
thrusting their heads far down the parent's gullet.

Two species are American: the brown pelican (*Pelecanus occidentalis*)
3½ to 4½ feet long, with bill gray and plumage gray-brown; and th
white pelican (*Pelecanus erythrorhynchos*), 4 to 5 feet long, and weighing
up to 30 pounds. The bill is yellow and the plumage white except fo
the black wing tips.

24

A colony of gannets (Morus bassanus)

BROWN PELICAN

Brown pelicans are the sort of birds whose quaint appearance inspires silly rhymes. As the bird sits asleep on a wharf piling, the bill points forward; when the bird is alert, the bill is drawn in against the neck as if straining for dignity. Flying along with measured, stately wing strokes, the pelican sees a fish, pushes its head forward and wings back and dives with a twist, disappearing underwater, and comes up facing the way it came. Draining the water from the bill, it swallows the fish. Then, lumbering, hopping and flapping, it takes off and joins a line of several of its fellows patrolling the waters just off the beaches. It is found all along the West Coast of the United States and along the East Coast north to the Carolinas, always near the shore.

WHITE PELICAN

One October evening just at dusk I stopped by a shallow lagoon on the Gulf Coast of northern Florida. Suddenly, I looked up to see a long line of great white birds filing by overhead: they were white pelicans migrating. They looked much larger than the 9-foot wingspread credited to them. Evidently they were coming from the western lakes, such as **Great Salt Lake**, where they breed, to winter on the Gulf coast. Other contingents from the same nesting grounds would fly to the California coast.

Unlike the brown pelican, the white pelican feeds by swimming. Sometimes it thrashes the water with its wings to stir the fish into activity, or flocks of the birds may line up and encircle a school of fish or drive them against the shore, the more easily to scoop them up in their huge bills.

Gannets and Boobies (*Family Sulidae*)

The gannets and boobies are large, gull-sized sea birds that fly over the water with stiff, rapid wing beats, dive from the air and swim underwater for fish. They have long, pointed wings, stout, tapered bills, pointed tails and all four toes webbed. They nest in colonies, lay one to three chalky blue-white eggs, and the young are fed there until full grown. The adults are boldly black or dark brown and white, whereas the young are more brownish and may take several years to become adult.

Only the gannet (*Morus bassanus*) is a regular part of our bird life. It is about three feet long, white with black wing tips and a yellow wash on its head. The young are gray-brown speckled with white.

On the Gaspé Peninsula of Quebec is a little village called Perce which, it is estimated, takes in $100,000 a year from tourists who come to see the gannet colony of about 13,000 nests on the nearby sanctuary of Bonaventure Island. The visitors go by motorboat along the base of the 400-foot cliffs whose ledges are white with the nesting birds; others wheel and soar everywhere overhead, and there is the continuous bedlam of their harsh calls. Farther offshore the birds are fishing. Flying as much as 100 feet above the water, a gannet sees a fish, partly closes its wings and dives, sending up a shower of spray as it hits the water; it submerges completely, seizes its prey and swallows it before coming to the surface. There are only a few other nesting sites in the western Atlantic, all in the Gulf of St. Lawrence—Newfoundland area. These gannets winter south to Florida's east coast, but are usually too far offshore to be seen from the land.

BOOBIES—CASUAL VISITORS

Tropical seas are the normal range of the boobies, but four species are recorded in the North American area. The blue-faced booby (*Sula dactylara*) visits Tortugas off Key West and has straggled to our southeast coast. The brown booby (*Sula leucogaster*) also visits Tortugas, is casual in Florida waters and sometimes wanders farther north. The other two species are the red-footed booby (*Sula sula*), which has been recorded on the Gulf of Mexico coast, and the blue-footed booby (*Sula nebouxii*), which has strayed to California.

Cormorants (*Family Phalacrocoracidae*)

The cormorants are black, duck- and goose-sized water birds that get their food of fish by swimming and diving in coastal ocean waters and in large rivers and lakes. The slender bill has a hook at the tip, the neck and tail are long and the toes are webbed. These birds swim low in the water with the tail submerged and the beak angled skyward. Dives are said to reach depths of several hundred feet, judging by cormorants caught in deep-water nets. Though cormorants use a hopping, splashing run for a takeoff, once they are awing their flight is strong and direct like that of a goose. Strangely, for a water bird, cormorants' plumage is not waterproof and they come ashore to sit with spread wings to dry.

Gregarious in feeding and in perching, they also nest in colonies, on sea cliffs, on islands, and in trees. The two to six eggs are chalky blue-green and the young are fed at the nest until full grown. In their first plumage the immature are browner than the adults.

There are six species of cormorants in America. Seen at a distance the ornamental crests are not evident and the adults appear all black. The species are best recognized by the differences in size and by the color of the bare skin of the face and throat. However, the great and the pelagic cormorant have white flank patches in breeding plumage.

DOUBLE-CRESTED CORMORANT

The name double-crested cormorant (*Phalacrocorax auritus*) recalls for me a dilapidated dock on the Gulf of Mexico with five cormorants perched on the roof of a shed. Their silhouettes are peculiar to the cormorant: upright posture of the elongate body, long tail, S-curved neck and up tilted head.

The double-crested cormorant has the widest range and the greatest adapt ability to habitat of any North American comormant and is the only one occurring in the interior of the continent. Its nesting colonies are found on grassy slopes of the Aleutian Islands, on flat islets in prairie lakes on swamp trees or islets in California, on cliff tops and in spruce tree overlooking the Gulf of St. Lawrence and in mangrove and cypress tree on the edge of heron rookeries in the Florida swamps. Not only are these cormorants gregarious in nesting but great rafts of them gather where small fish abound, as in the Gulf of Mexico and San Francisco Bay. The double-crested cormorant is a medium-sized species, 33 inches long, all black with a yellow face and throat.

OTHER CORMORANTS

Two other cormorants occur on the Atlantic coast, the olivaceous cormo rant (*Phalacrocorax olivaceus*) of Central America, which ranges north to the Texas coast, and the great cormorant (*Phalacrocorax carbo*), up to 40 inches long, which nests on sea-facing cliffs in eastern Canada and

Left: *Anhinga (Anhinga anhinga)*
Right: *Double-crested cormorant (Phalacrocorax auritus)*

29

winters south along the coast to New York. On the Pacific coast there are three saltwater cormorants. The small, slender pelagic cormorant (*Phalacrocorax pelagicus*), 27 inches long, feeds in deep offshore waters and chooses inaccessible little ledges and grottos on sea cliffs for its small colonies. The larger, more robust Brandt's cormorant (*Phalacrocorax penicillatus*), 34 inches long, feeds in inshore waters and even dives in the surf. It is the cormorant commonly seen perched on buoys and rocks, and nests in large colonies on ledges of sea cliffs. The third species, the red-faced cormorant (*Phalacrocorax urile*), lives about the islands of the Bering Sea.

Anhinga (*Family Anhingidae*)

The anhinga (*Anhinga anhinga*) is a swimming and diving bird of freshwater lakes, ponds and lagoons in our southeastern states and southward. It is about 27 inches long, with big webbed feet, a long slender neck and head, a sharp-pointed bill and a long broad tail. The plumage is black with silvery streaks in the forepart of the wing and the female has a pale brown head and neck.

Driving in south Florida one sees solitary birds swimming in brush- or tree-edged ponds near the road, often with only the head and neck showing above the water, sometimes with a sunfish that has been speared underwater in its bill. More conspicuous are anhingas drying their outstretched wings on fenceposts or dead branches. Sometimes one or more birds soar high overhead, whereupon the slender head and neck and ample wings and tail give a striking silhouette.

The nest of sticks, singly or in a small loose colony, is placed in a tree; four blue-green eggs are laid and the young are cared for in the nest.

Frigate or Man-o'-War Birds
(*Family Fregatidae*)

The occasional magnificent man-o'-war bird (*Fregata magnificens*) sailing high over southern Florida or California coasts is a visitor from more tropical waters. Its shape is most distinctive: a small body; narrow, angled wings with a 7-foot spread; long, deeply forked tail and a long bill with a hook at the tip; and an overall length of more than 3 feet. The males are black with an inflatable orange, gular pouch used in courtship; the females and young have a variable amount of white in the plumage.

Though the small feet are partly webbed and all the food comes from the sea, the birds do not voluntarily alight on the water. Rather, flying low, they snatch fish and sometimes young terns with their hooked bills. More often, however, frigate birds harry flying terns or boobies until they disgorge their prey and then the frigate birds swoop down and seize this secondhand food. For the night, frigate birds gather to roost on mangrove and other sea-edge trees.

Herons and Bitterns *(Family Ardeidae)*

The flooded pastures in the cabbage palm country of south Florida are the best places I know in which to watch herons. From the road one sees white patches that recall snow banks to the northern visitor but they turn out to be groups of white herons, snowy egrets, common egrets and young little blue herons. By stopping and looking carefully one also may see dark herons nearby: Louisiana herons, adult little blue herons and an occasional great blue heron. On dryer pastures occasional swarms of white cattle egrets swirl among the cattle they attend, and a little green heron may be prowling the edge of a nearby pond. Two other herons, the great white heron and the reddish egret, must be sought farther south, on the shores of Florida bays.

The southeastern states are the headquarters of the herons, where all thirteen species occur, and to which some are restricted. Others are more widely distributed wherever suitable habitats exist but only two, the great blue heron and the bittern, go much beyond the Canadian border.

Herons range from 12 to 48 inches long, and are long-legged birds with long necks and dagger-like bills adapted for wading and spearing fish. But each species has its own feeding techniques, from watchful waiting to active hunting, and not only fish but any small animal, vertebrate or invertebrate, may be taken. Some species, especially the snowy egret and the cattle egret, like to feed in flocks and some gather in certain trees to roost.

31

Gregariousness is most apparent in the heron rookeries. The folk name of "crane towns" aptly indicates their nature. In a mass of willows, a clump of mangrove trees, or in stands of cypress, the closely spaced nests may number in the hundreds or thousands, and in addition to half a dozen species of herons a rookery may have neighborhoods of nesting ibis, cormorants and even pelicans. The heron's nest is a rather flat structure of sticks built by both parents. Courtship goes on here, and after the eggs are laid one parent is always at home. The downy young are fed in the nest or among the branches to which half-grown young scramble. The food is brought from the marshes in the parent's gullet and regurgitated for the young. A heron rookery is a noisy place resounding with the squawks of alarm, courtship, quarreling and the begging of the young. The colony is also a smelly place because of the droppings and the fallen scraps of food.

After the breeding season is over there is a strange exodus of some herons, apparently in every direction, which may find birds such as common egrets far north of their breeding grounds. But with cold weather and freezing waters, northern populations move south, though no species leaves the United States completely.

SLATY-COLORED HERONS

In the southern marshes the great blue heron (*Ardea herodias*) is only one of many herons feeding in marsh, pond or shoreline. But in the north, across the continent, the great blue is "the heron" even if it is often called "blue crane" and a rookery is sometimes known as "crane town." This bird's main feeding habitat is fish-producing shallow water, salt or fresh, and where there are trees it nests in them in colonies. Where trees are lacking, as near lakes and marshes in the arid West, the birds may place their nest on the ground on an islet or even on rocks or cliff tops. The great blue is our largest heron, 48 inches long, and mostly gray in color.

Favoring tidal flats and freshwater marshes of the southeastern states, the little blue heron (*Florida caerulea*), 25 inches long, is one of the common small herons and is generally slaty blue. For its small size it is rather stodgy and slow moving as it wades along in shallow water or on land looking for its prey. Unlike the other herons the young are all white and resemble egrets.

The Louisiana heron (*Hydranassa tricolor*), 26 inches long, is slaty gray with a white belly. It has the same range as the little blue heron, is even

Top: Cattle egret (Bubulcus ibis)
Bottom: Louisiana heron (Hydranassa tricolor)

nore common, and the two species often feed in the same marsh, fly in he same flock and nest in the same big rookery. Yet there is a whole series of differences. The Louisiana heron is less shy, is slimmer and more active, often has its neck extended on short flights, wades in deeper water and s more common in freshwater than in saltwater habitats.

Restricted to the coasts of southern Florida and Texas, the reddish egret (*Dichromanassa rufescens*) favors the tidal flats and nearby freshwater agoons and is the least abundant of our herons. Like the snowy egret, t is an active species, dashing about through the shallow water, making sudden turns and short flights in pursuing small fishes. Occasionally a white color phase occurs, but the normal plumage is slate with the neck reddish.

WHITE HERONS AND EGRETS

There are four species of herons or egrets in which the plumage is entirely white: the cattle egret of the southeast; the snowy and common egret in the southern part of the continent; and the great white heron of south Florida. Two other species have white color phases.

A native of the Old World, the cattle egret (*Bubulcus ibis*) first appeared n the United States in 1952 and has proved an amazingly successful immigrant in the southeastern part of the country. On a visit to south Florida n 1969 I found it the most conspicuous widespread heron. Flocks totaling hundreds of birds occupied a single large pasture, swirling among the pines, searching for grasshoppers in the dry grass, accompanying grazing cattle for the sake of the insects the beasts stirred into activity, or resting n the shade next to dozing cows, and sometimes even perching on their backs. The cattle egret is a small white heron, 20 inches long, with a stout yellow bill and pale feet, and in breeding dress has a tan tinge on crown and breast.

The nuptial plumes, a tuft on the head, another on the breast, and one of elongated filmy feathers recurved at the tip, make the snowy egret (*Leucophoyx thula*) the most elaborately decorated of our herons. These plumes are used in mutual displays in courtship and in nest relief ceremonies. Sometimes when quarrels arise in a resting party of birds the plumes are also raised.

The snowy egret is the most active and agile of the white herons. While some birds may stand in groups at the water's edge and others walk

Top: Reddish egret (Dichromanassa rufescens)
Bottom: Snowy egret (Leucophoyx thula)

sedately through the shallow water, every now and then a few birds may run skittishly through the water. Traveling on an irregular course, now in one direction, now in another, with occasional flicks of partly spread wings as if to maintain balance, the birds jab here and there for surprised prey.

The snowy egret, 25 inches long, has black bill and legs with contrasting yellow toes.

Often the common egret (*Casmerodius albus*) is tame enough to allow a car to park near it and watch it feeding in a flooded grass-grown roadside ditch. The bird then carries its neck extended forward with head bent down at a curious angle and walks with slow steps and frequent pauses to examine each bit of cover for some luckless water animal, fish, frog or insect. The common egret is a medium-sized white heron, 39 inches long, with a slender head and neck, yellow bill and black legs and feet. A long tuft of straight, long plumes on the lower back is the common egret's only decoration.

The great white heron (*Ardea occidentalis*) is an uncommon bird, limited in its distribution to the Florida Bay area where I have seen it from the northern end of the Overseas Highway to Key West. It is a very large bird and its form and habits are like those of the great blue heron, of which some students would consider it a local color phase. Two other herons have white color phases: the rare reddish egrets in adult plumage and the little blue heron in its immature plumage.

GREEN HERON

The coloration of the green heron (*Butorides virescens*) is distinctive: black crown, red-brown neck, green wings and grayish brown underparts. It is small in size—19 inches long. But its form and behavior are still more striking. The long feathers of the neck hide its curves so that it seems a dumpy bird, lacking the grace of most other herons. Even so, some of its poses seem peculiar. Notable is its horizontal stance, with legs bent so that its body and head are close to the water or mud as it watches for, or stalks, its prey. In addition to feeding on open marshes and shores, this little heron forages along tiny streams and small patches of marsh in wooded country. When alarmed it flies with rapid wing beats and startled "skeow's" to perch in a tree. The range of this species includes the eastern half of the country and also the regions west of the plains.

Common egret (Casmerodius albus)

37

NIGHT HERONS

At a midwestern marshy pond in late summer I once watched a group of common egrets feeding until dusk, when they left for their night roost in a distant swampy forest. Barely had the egrets left when a straggling line of black-crowned herons (*Nycticorax nycticorax*) came from their day roost in the swampy forest, scattered over the marsh and began stalking about and watching for something to move in the water. They took over where the egrets left off — the night shift as it were. Soon it was too dark to see how night herons fished, but apparently they may move from marsh to marsh at night, for their "quock" calls as they go overhead in the darkness is a common sound.

As one might expect of night birds, the night herons have big heads and large eyes. The adult black-crowned night heron is black above with gray wings and whitish underparts and two narrow white head plumes. The lesser known yellow-crowned night heron (*Nyctanassa violacea*) of the eastern United States is gray above and below with black markings on the back and a black, yellow and whitish head. The young of both are streaked recalling the character of bitterns.

BITTERNS

The spring "song" of the American bittern (*Botaurus lentiginosus*) is a series of loud, liquid thumps and squelches that harmonizes well with its marshy habitat and is heard more often than the bird is seen. It lives a solitary secretive life among the grasses and reeds of freshwater marshes and against such a background its patterned brown, buffy and black plumage is ideal camouflage. Occasionally I have been fortunate enough to watch a bittern feeding undisturbed. One was prowling knee-deep in the watery edge of a marsh, taking very slow, deliberate steps with occasional pauses bent over with head thrust forward and watching everywhere for fish, frog or insect. Another time a bittern prowling a grassy meadow jabbed into the grass and brought up a meadow mouse, which it held by the head.

The American bittern, 28 inches long, makes a solitary nest in the reeds and is the most northern American heron, nesting north to near timber line. The related least bittern (*Ixobrychus exilis*), 12 inches long, is a much smaller, rarer, and secretive bird of the reed beds north to the Canadian border.

Storks and Wood Ibis (*Family Ciconiidae*)

My interest in the wood ibis (*Mycteria americana*) was first aroused by seeing a lone bird in a flooded tomato field in south Florida. It walked along between the rows, stopping now and then to hold its half-opened bill in the water, and balance on one foot while it used the other to chase small water animals into the bill, whereupon the mandibles snapped shut. Later I found that this was one of the two ways the wood ibis fed. The other way, in more open water, was to walk along with the open bill in the water until prey was encountered by chance, a method of feeding that could only have been developed where the water was rich in food.

The wood ibis is the only North American stork, and most of this species in the United States nest in Florida; in 1960 the largest colony, in Corkscrew Swamp, had 5,000 nests and produced an estimated 14,500 young. But, depending on the weather, productivity varies, and in some years no young are raised. The feeding grounds are expanses of shallow water swarming with life and may be 25 miles from the stork nests in the cypress trees of the colony. Some birds leave the colony early in the day and make the journey to feeding grounds by alternately flapping their great broad wings and gliding. The wood ibis usually flies and feeds in flocks.

Sometimes a routine is followed on the feeding grounds. After feeding to repletion in the morning the storks walk to dry land and rest until the heat of the day causes rising currents of air called thermals. Then the storks fly into these currents and on motionless wings soar up until they are barely visible to the naked eye.

The wood ibis, 40 inches long, is a white bird with black in its wings, a naked blackish head, long legs, neck and bill and long broad wings. Though at present breeding is restricted to Florida and tropical America, birds wander to California, the Carolinas and occasionally northward.

Ibises and Spoonbills (*Family Threskiornithidae*)

Like herons, ibises are found in the wetlands and are long-legged, long-necked, long-billed wading birds. But unlike herons they are plump-breast-

Overleaf: Left: Wood ibis (Mycteria americana)
Top right: Roseate spoonbill (Ajaia ajaja)
Bottom right: American flamingoes (Phoenicopterus ruber)

ed and walk actively about hunting their food in mud, marsh or shallow water. They fly with their necks extended and are not only gregarious but feed in flocks and often fly in formation. The nests are in trees or among reeds or even on the ground on islets and they may be found in big mixed rookeries of herons. The four American ibises are 22-25 inches long and have long, slender downcurved bills; the single spoonbill, 32 inches long, has a long bill expanded spoonlike at the tip.

IBISES

A flock of white ibises (*Eudocimus albus*) feeding in a wet meadow or a mudflat presents a picture of industry, the birds walking along probing and grubbing in the mud for their favorite food of crayfish, though grasshoppers, snails, earthworms, and frogs do not go neglected. The feeding grounds are often far from their roosts or nesting places and the flock fly in characteristic V-formation or lines. The beating of their black-tipped wings is often interrupted by periods of gliding on set wings. The ibises nest in trees or in reeds in dense colonies that may contain hundreds of thousands of nests. Sometimes white ibises nest in heron rookeries and the ibis nests are likely to be grouped by themselves in a separate "neighborhood."

Though the adult plumage is mostly white, the wing tips are black and at breeding time the bill and feet are red. The immature are brown and white. In the United States they are found in the southeast from Florida to eastern Texas.

At a distance the related glossy ibis (*Plegadis falcinellus*) of Florida and the white-faced glossy ibis (*Plegadis chihi*) of the marshes of Texas and the western marshes both appear black, the bronzy brown tinge being evident only at close range. Both occur in great numbers locally. The scarlet ibis (*Eudocimus ruber*), a tropical species with scarlet plumage and black-tipped wings, has been recorded in the southeastern states.

ROSEATE SPOONBILL

One October I saw roseate spoonbills (*Ajaia ajaja*) come to roost for the night in a shallow, mangrove-enclosed lagoon. They came by twos and threes with the setting sun shining behind their wings and turning their pink to flame just before they dropped below the tops of the trees and glided down to join those already standing in the open water. Earlier in

Trumpeter swans (Olor buccinator)

he day I had watched them feeding on flooded mudflats of nearby Florida
Bay, walking along, the partly open bill submerged and swinging back and
orth through the water and thin mud, feeling for small aquatic animals.
When a fish or crustacean slipped between the spoon-shaped tips of the
mandibles, the bill was snapped shut and the prey caught.

A tropical species, the roseate spoonbill reaches its farthest north in
Florida and on the Texas coast. It nests in small numbers in colonies, in
rees, or even on the ground on islets.

Flamingoes *(Family Phoenicopteridae)*

magine if you will a pink-plumaged bird with a body as large as that of
a goose, a neck longer than that of a swan, a short, stout bill sharply

bent downward in the middle, legs longer than a stork's but with webbed feet. Such is the flamingo.

The American flamingo (*Phoenicopterus ruber*), 4 feet from bill to tail tip, lives on extensive mudflats covered with shallow salt or brackish water. Here it wades and sieves small aquatic organisms from the water and mud and here the birds nest on the tops of truncate cones they build above the water by scooping mud from the bottom.

The flamingo is strongly gregarious in feeding and in nesting, and it flies about in great flocks. In flight, the black in the wings contrasts with its general pink plumage. The birds' normal range is from West Indian islands and Yucatan southward. In bygone years large flocks visited the shallow waters of Florida Bay. Some may have nested. Occasional birds are still seen in south Florida but some, perhaps most, are probably escapees from flocks kept as ornamental waterfowl at such places as Hialeah Racetrack near Miami.

Swans, Geese and Ducks (*Family Anatidae*)

There is something especially thrilling in the sight and sound of water-fowl. It may be the clamor of wild geese passing overhead, a line of long-necked swans moving along the edge of lake ice, a skein of uneasy mallard and pintails making preliminary excursions at dusk about a marsh before taking off on the next leg of their migration, a swarm of a dozen species of ducks over a nesting ground by a prairie slough, or the gyrations and chattering of flocks of old squaws who have newly arrived at their winter quarters.

Waterfowl range in size from the 13-inch-long teal to the 6-foot-long trumpeter swan. They have stout bodies, short legs, webbed feet, long necks and flattened bills, moderate wings and waterproof plumage. Their main adaptation is for swimming and for sieving small food items from mud or water. But they also walk well and have great powers of flight.

Most of the fifty or so species in North America north of Mexico nest in the West and Northwest by prairie and tundra ponds. They winter in the South, especially in such areas as the Carolina coast, the Gulf of Mexico marshes and the interior valleys of California. Most species nest on the

Black-bellied tree duck (Dendrocygna autumnalis

ground and the female lines her nest with down she plucks from her breast she lays two to sixteen buff, greenish or white eggs that she incubates. The downy young are active from hatching and are cared for by the female or by both parents.

SWANS

There are two native species and one introduced species of swans in North America. One of the two native species is the whistling swan (*Olor columbianus*).

Whistling Swan

A great white bird, larger than any goose and with a much longer neck, the whistling swan has been able to survive the European colonization of America by nesting on the Arctic barrens where civilization has not reached and by making few stops on its long flight to its wintering grounds on the mid-Atlantic and Pacific coast areas. One of the best-known stopping places on migration is on Lake Erie and another is the Bear River marshes of Utah. But occasionally a small party or even a single bird stops on some small lake or pond where it dwarfs the ducks and ignores them. The swans travel in lines or a wedge-shaped formation and their voices are somewhat like those of Canada geese but more musical or whistle-like.

The whistling swan is a vegetarian, feeding in shallow water where it can reach the pond weed and roots, tipping up, tail pointed skyward like a mallard, when necessary. The birds pair for life and the nest is a heaped up mound of grass and moss; family duties are shared by both parents. The adults may reach nearly 5 feet in length and weigh up to about 20 pounds. The bill is black, and there is ordinarily a yellow spot in front of the eye.

Trumpeter Swan

The other of our native species is the trumpeter swan (*Olor buccinator*). The trumpeter swan is our largest swan, measuring up to 6 feet long and averaging about 30 pounds in weight. Its original breeding range was across the northern part of the country and the Northwest, where man's settlements made extinction inevitable. In 1933 only 66 individuals survived in the United States. Since then, protection and sanctuaries have

46

slowly increased this number so that there are probably several thousand individuals in the northwestern states where they are non-migratory, and in western Canada and Alaska where they make short migrations. Besides its larger size the trumpeter swan differs from the whistling swan in having a black bill and no yellow spot in front of the eye.

The mute swan (*Cygnus olor*), introduced from Europe, is the common swan of city parks and is different from both the trumpeter and whistler in having the bill partly pink. It is established in some Middle Atlantic states, but occasionally pairs are found breeding in surprisingly remote, more western areas.

GEESE

Smaller than swans and larger than many ducks, geese have smaller feet and shorter necks than swans. They sometimes feed on open ground, grazing on green vegetation. Unlike most ducks, the sexes are alike, the pairing may be for life, and both male and female share the responsibility of caring for the nest and the young. In North America seven species of geese occur regularly, of which the Canada goose is the best known.

Canada Goose

To most Americans across the continent the Canada goose (*Branta canadensis*) is known simply as "the wild goose," and the wedge-shaped flocks of honking wild geese that in spring and autumn pass over town and country by day and night provide a moving accompaniment to the change of the seasons. The "honkers" may have wintered on the coastal marshes of the Atlantic or the marshes, lagoons and lakes of the Midwest, the Gulf of Mexico, Mexico, interior valleys of California and along the Pacific coast north to British Columbia. They graze on green vegetation or, morning and evening, fly out to feed on waste grain in harvested fields and the newly sprouted greenery of planted fields. Always there are lookouts, birds more wary than the rest, that sound the alarm, "honk-a-honk," and send the whole flock with a babble of calls fleeing to open water or a sandbar.

Canada geese migrate early; sometimes flocks seem to go on exploratory flights looking for open water. The birds nest over much of Canada and in the northern part of the United States by prairie lakes, marshy ponds and on arctic barrens. The birds mate for life. The male guards the incubating female on the nest, which is a mass of vegetation on the ground, and when the five to six creamy white eggs hatch, both parents accompany the goslings, the pugnacity of the gander foiling many a predator. While the young are growing their flight feathers, the adults moult theirs and are also flightless for a time. Fully winged, the family remains a unit, joins other families from the same area and sets off for their ancestral wintering grounds. This clannishness has resulted in many subspecies. The largest goose, 3½ feet long and weighing up to 18 pounds, nests on the prairies, whereas the smallest, about 22 inches long and weighing only 5 pounds, nests in far northern Alaska. Medium-sized subspecies live in intermediate areas. Some of the large, more southern birds may migrate a short distance, while some of the smallest make the longest migrations—as much as 4,000 miles. All of them are grayish to brownish, have a black head and a neck set off by a distinctive white patch across cheeks and throat. Canada geese do well in captivity and are commonly kept as ornamental waterfowl. Some of these escape and return to the wild.

Other Geese

There are six other species of geese that nest on the Arctic barrens and winter in the United States.

The brant (*Branta bernicla*) of the eastern Arctic winters along the eastern coast and is about 26 inches long and similar to the Canada goose, with head and neck black, but the white is restricted to a patch on each side of the neck.

The black brant (*Branta nigricans*) of the western Arctic winters along the Pacific coast and is like the brant but with a black breast and belly.

The white-fronted goose (*Anser albifrons*) of the Arctic migrates chiefly through the central part of the continent to winter on the Gulf of Mexico marshes, though some migrate down the Pacific coast to California. It is a gray bird about 30 inches long. The adult has a white forehead and the immature have irregular black markings on the underparts.

The snow goose (*Chen hyperborea*), which nests in the Arctic, has one population of large birds that winter on the Atlantic coast. Most of the others go directly south to the marshes of the Gulf of Mexico or of Califor-

Top: *Canada goose* (*Branta canadensis*)
Bottom: *Mallard* (*Anas platyrhynchos*)

nia and Oregon. It is white with black wing tips and ranges from 24 to 36 inches in length. The blue goose (*Chen caerulescens*) nests with the snow goose in the central Arctic and winters with it in Gulf of Mexico marshes. Some students think it is only a color phase of the snow goose, since it differs from the latter in being mostly bluish, with head and upper neck all white. The Ross's goose (*Chen rossii*), nesting in a small area in the central Arctic and migrating in a narrow flyway overland to California, is like a small snow goose but with a warty base to the bill.

There are two other geese in America: the Emperor goose (*Philacte canagica*) of the Bering Sea area, which is 27 inches long and much like a blue goose in color but with a black chin and throat, and the barnacle goose (*Branta leucopsis*), 26 inches long, a small relative of the Canada goose but with the white of its chin and cheeks more extensive and covering the forehead. It sometimes visits the eastern United States.

TREE DUCKS

Tree ducks are a tropical group with many traits like geese, such as sexes that are alike, moulting only once a year, and both sexes sharing family cares. Their name comes from the habit some species have of roosting in trees. They are also called whistling ducks because of their calls. Two species range from Mexico into the southern United States. The black-bellied tree duck (*Dendrocygna autumnalis*), 20 inches long, is a reddish brown and black bird with a pink bill and a big white area in the upper surface of the wing. It ranges to south Texas. The fulvous tree duck (*Dendrocygna bicolor*), with tawny head and underparts and with black and buffy barred back, ranges from Mexico north to coastal Texas, Louisiana and central California. Some farmers consider the species a pest because of its activities in fields of rice and other crops where it nests.

SURFACE-FEEDING DUCKS

The surface-feeding ducks or pond ducks spring directly into flight from land or water and rarely dive. These ducks reach food in water by "tipping up" and by sieving vegetation and small aquatic invertebrates from near the surface. Some of them, like the mallard and black duck, also fly to stubble fields for grain. Brilliant males and dull females is the rule for most species; when the females start incubating, the drakes desert them and undergo a moult into what is called an eclipse plumage very like

Gadwalls (*Anas strepera*)

that of the female. While in this dull plumage all the flight feathers are
shed and the birds are flightless for a time.

The sequence of the species is as follows: mallard; black ducks; teals;
other prairie pond ducks; and wood duck.

Mallard

The mallard (*Anas platyrhynchos*), the wild ancestor of the green-headed
drake of the barnyard, is perhaps the best-known duck over much of
the northern hemisphere. It is also highly prized by the sportsman
crouching in a blind among the reeds of a shallow pond or a marsh,
or by a field where the birds come morning and evening to eat waste
grain. I have felt the excitement of the whistling swish of mallard wings
pitching over a blind. Equally vivid is the glimpse of a small flock of
mallards guzzling bits of floating vegetation from the surface and then
all suddenly tipping up, tails pointed skyward and orange feet paddling
half in, half out of the water as they tear loose submerged water weeds.

In America the mallard is largely a bird of the central and western
part of the continent, where it nests north to the edge of the Arctic
barrens. In recent years it has become more common in the eastern
states, perhaps the result of the release of captive birds. One of the
mallard's winter headquarters is the lower Mississippi Valley south to
the Gulf Coast. Sometimes flooded river bottom forests with an abundance of acorns may attract large numbers; others winter on salt marshes.

Black Ducks

There are three close relatives of the mallard in which both sexes resemble very dark female mallards and behave like mallards: the black duck (*Anas rubripes*) of the eastern third of the continent, nesting in the north and wintering in the south; the Mexican duck (*Anas diazi*) whose northern limit is in the Rio Grande Valley, and the mottled duck (*Anas fulvigula*) of Florida.

Teals

The smallest pond ducks, 13-17 inches long, are called teals. The smallest of these, the 13-14 inch long green-winged teal (*Anas carolinensis*), is the most agile awing. When a small flock leaves the water, the birds go up faster and at a more vertical angle than other ducks and then fly over the reeds at an amazing speed, keeping close together and synchronizing their turns and twists very much like some shore birds. The male has a cinnamon head with a green face patch and nests in the West and Northwest. The related common teal (*Anas crecca*) of the Old World nests in the Aleutian Islands and has strayed to the American mainland.

The blue-winged teal (*Anas discors*), in which the male has a white crescent on the face and a blue shoulder patch, nests in the Middle West and to the west and north, while the closely related cinnamon teal (*Anas cyanoptera*), with head, neck and body cinnamon red in the male, is a more western species whose range overlaps that of the bluewing.

Other Prairie Pond Ducks

In addition to the large mallard and the small teal that nest abundantly in the lakes, ponds, potholes and marshes of the prairies of the north and west, there are four other pond ducks of medium size that commonly nest in those areas and winter in the southern United States and southward. These are: the gadwall (*Anas strepera*), a gray duck with a white speculum; the pintail (*Anas acuta*), a slender species of which the drake has long pointed central tail feathers; the shoveler (*Spatula clypeata*), with a long bill broadened at the tip; and the American widgeon (*Mareca americana*), of which the drake has a white crown. The related European widgeon (*Mareca penelope*), the male of which has a pinkish buffy crown and cinnamon cheeks, visits the North American continent so frequently that it has been suggested but never proved that it breeds in America.

Wood duck (Aix sponsa)

Wood Duck

One of the loveliest sights I can recall is a mated pair of wood ducks (*Aix sponsa*) in a patch of spring sunshine on a log across a stream. The sheen of the male's metallic blue, green and purple upperparts and the deep red-brown breast and buffy flanks changed with every move of the bird, the plumage set off by the purple crest and the white lines of the throat and the side of the head and the narrow white lines of the flank feathers. This duck's plumage is as unique as its favorite nesting habitat— dark wooded streams. Flying through the river bottom forest the pair chose a hollow in a sycamore which the female lined with down from her breast. When she began to incubate the male left her to moult in a nearby marshy pond. When the young hatched and hopped out of the nest, the mother led them on foot to the same pond. When all were full winged and flew from pond to marsh or bottomland forest, the large head and the long tail and white belly made recognition easy.

The range of the wood duck is strangely divided: a permanent Pacific coast population and a population in the eastern part of the country which goes to the Gulf of Mexico coastal marshes for the winter.

DIVING DUCKS

On their wintering grounds, which is where they are generally seen, diving ducks usually gather in flocks on open water. There they dive for their food and sleep. Unlike pond ducks, diving ducks need a long pattering run over the surface of the water for a take-off.

The sequence of species is as follows: ring-neck duck, canvasback, red head and scaup; goldeneyes and bufflehead; old squaw; harlequin; ei ders; scoters; ruddy ducks and mergansers.

Ring-necked Duck, Canvasback, Redhead and Scaup

The ring-necked duck and its four close relatives are flocking, diving ducks, 14-20 inches long. At an earlier period they were known chiefly a game for the fowler; and the canvasback, particularly when it had been feeding on wild celery, was esteemed as a course in a banquet. Now bird watchers far outnumber the fowlers.

Changes in the range and abundance of certain birds is well known and certainly applies to the ring-necked duck (*Aythya collaris*). But the pictur of the ring-neck's past is beclouded by the fact that the old-time gunner confused it with the lesser scaup. Only with the rise of modern bird-watching and field identification was it realized how easy the males are to identify. Originally considered to breed only in western Canada, the ring-neck is now known to nest across the continent in the north and winter on fresh waters in the Southwest and the Southeast. I have known it best in the Middle West when it is on spring migration. It arrives in small flocks after the mallards and pintails have left and it lingers on the little ponds for some weeks, diving for its food but not engaging in courtship activity. Along with the ringneck are a few redheads, canvasbacks and lesser scaups, feeding in the same way but generally ignoring the small ponds.

The drake redhead (*Aythya americana*) and canvasback (*Aythya valisine-ria*) both have red-brown heads and necks, but the redhead has a dish-faced profile and the canvasback a straight profile. Their nurseries are in the ponds and marshes of the Canadian prairies and northward. Both species seem to make long distance overland flights with few stops to their main wintering grounds on brackish coastal waters. There they assemble in large flocks and dive for aquatic vegetation. The greater scaup (*Aythya marila*), with a blackish head and neck and white flanks, nests in the far Northwest and winters along the coast, often in saltwater where marine invertebrates bulk large in its diet. The very similar but smaller lesser scaup (*Aythya affinis*) also nests in the Northwest and in winter assembles in great rafts on fresh and sheltered saltwater in the South where it is locally the most abundant duck. The ring-neck drake differs from the scaup in having a black back, gray flanks and a white bar in front of the wing.

Goldeneyes and Bufflehead

The males of the two goldeneyes and the bufflehead are boldly patterned in black and white. Winter visitors to coastal bays and inland waters, they are stout diving ducks that are usually scattered along the shore singly, in pairs or small parties. In flight the wings of the goldeneyes sometimes make a whistling noise that on a hazy morning may announce the approach of the birds before they come into view. The bufflehead, only 14 inches long, is especially active in its diving, going down and coming up so suddenly that it seems to bounce.

On Lake Michigan in February one of the first signs of spring is the common goldeneye (*Bucephala clangula*) engaged in courtship. One male

of a mixed party fluffs out its head feathers, stretches the head forward, snaps it back, gives a harsh "zzee-at" and then with a flash of orange feet surges ahead. The female finally responds, a pair is formed, and the birds go north till they find a hole in a tree by a northern lake for a nest.

In the common goldeneye, 18 inches long, the male has a black head with a round white spot in front of the eye, while the female has a red-brown head. The Barrow's goldeneye (*Bucephala islandica*) has a crescent-shaped eye spot. The drake of the smaller bufflehead (*Bucephala albeola*) has a white band across the back of the head, while the duck has a black head with a white spot back of the eye. All three species nest north of most settlements.

Old Squaw

When the zero weather of January closes the last of the Arctic waters and drives the old squaws (*Clangula hyemalis*) from the far north where they nest on the ground, the birds appear in flocks of thousands on our northern coasts and on the Great Lakes. From a Lake Michigan pier I have seen as many as 10,000 and perhaps 20,000 birds at once, some on the water, but most in long lines and swirling flocks, flying swiftly to and fro as if in a state of great excitement. Their chattering and cackling was a vivid demonstration of how they got their name. The drake is more white than black-brown in winter, but is the reverse in summer. The drake is also the only diving duck with a long pointed tail; that is why it is 23 inches while the female is only 17 inches long.

Harlequin Duck

Favoring rocks and rough water, the harlequin (*Histrionicus histrionicus*) nests along streams in the northwestern mountains and in Labrador; in winter it moves to rocky coasts where the surf pounds on headlands, islets and reefs. At a distance the harlequin duck, 16 inches long, appears to be a dark bird although the drake has rufous flanks and nine white patches scattered on each side from a crescent in front of the eye to a spot at the base of the tail. The female, by contrast, is dark and drab, with three white spots on the side of the head.

Eiders

Eider ducks are stout diving ducks of the Arctic, where they nest near the

Top: *Canvasback drake* (*Aythya valisineria*)
Bottom: *Drake redhead* (*Aythya americana*)

edge of the sea or by tundra ponds. In winter they move southward, but no farther than the coasts of our northern states, where they mass offshore in big flocks and dive to the bottom for shellfish. The males are black and white or black, white and brown, while the females are brown barred or have a blackish mottling.

There are outposts of nesting common eiders (*Somateria mollissima*) in northern Maine and on the Alaska peninsula but the main breeding range is in the Arctic. There the birds nest in colonies near the sea, preferring low rocky islets safe from Arctic foxes. Like many ducks the female lines her nest with down plucked from her breast. Locally, in Iceland and in arctic Canada, this down is harvested, cleaned and sent to market as eiderdown for use in making light, warm sleeping robes and jackets.

When the young hatch, some stay with the parent but some walk down to the sea by themselves and apparently attach themselves to any female that will accept them; large mixed broods may be presided over by a single duck who is not a parent at all. In late autumn these eiders are common off the New England coast, where they dive over the mussel beds of the outlying reefs and islands. Sometimes they come ashore at low tide but fly out to sleep on the open sea. The common eider drake, up to 26 inches long, has the back mostly white, the lower breast and belly black.

The king eider (*Somateria spectabilis*) of the central Arctic nests by tundra ponds. Although in winter it is not common off our northern coasts, it does straggle to the Great Lakes. The male has a black back. There are two other eiders that are found only in the Bering Sea area: the spectacled eider (*Lampronetta fischeri*), in which the male has a white eye patch outlined in black; and the Steller's eider (*Polysticta stelleri*), in which the male has the breast and belly brown.

Scoters

The scoters are stout-bodied, thick-necked diving ducks measuring from 17 to 23 inches long; the males are black above and below and the females mostly brownish. The three species nest in the West or Northwest and and winter off both coasts. Their migrations are overland and many individuals stop off where freshwater is available on their routes.

I first knew the white-winged scoter (*Melanitta deglandi*) in winter flocks waiting off northern coasts for the tide to cover the mussel beds with the right depth of water. Then the birds would swim out and dive for the shellfish. It seemed incongruous to find these northern birds in summer on the prairie ponds of the West and Northwest, nesting in the great wild-fowl nurseries along with teal and scaup, ruddy duck and gadwall. But it did illustrate the great seasonal changes in diets and habitats made by a great many migrating birds.

The white-wing scoter has a conspicuous white patch on its wing. The male of the related surf scoter (*Melanitta perspicillata*) has a white patch on the back of the head but the common scoter (*Oidemia nigra*), nesting farther north, has all-black plumage.

Ruddy Ducks

A tubby little duck floating low in the water with its tail sticking straight up can only be a ruddy duck (*Oxyura jamaicensis*). Both the brownish female with white cheeks and the full-plumaged drake with plumage mostly red-brown but also with white cheeks and black crown have this

Common merganser (Mergus merganser)

slightly ludicrous appearance. Its summer home is on the ponds of the prairies and it winters chiefly on salt water.

The related masked duck (*Oxyura dominica*) of Mexico occasionally reaches south Texas.

Mergansers

Mergansers are fish-eaters that dive and chase their prey underwater. Appropriately, their bodies are elongated, less tubby than those of most diving ducks, and their bills are long, narrow, and provided with toothlike serrations to aid in holding slippery fish.

In November, the common (*Mergus merganser*) and red-breasted (*Mergus serrator*) mergansers from the north, all in dull winter dress, arrive on their winter quarters. Long lines of the gray, brown-headed birds move over the waves. Although unmistakably large ducks, the small heads, thin bill, long bodies and slashing flight give them a distinctly rakish appearance. When a flock alights and begins feeding, the birds often dive with a forward leap that carries them clear of the surface. Later in the winter, drakes in full plumage appear. The common merganser male has a black head without a crest and white underparts with a pink tinge that show perfectly when several drakes rest on a cake of floating ice. The red-breasted merganser drake has a ragged crest on its black head and a red-brown patch on its breast. In both species the female has a brown head and crest.

The common merganser nests across the continent chiefly in wooded parts of Canada, laying its eggs in a hole in a tree near freshwater, and winters on freshwater and saltwater across the northern parts of the country. The red-breasted merganser nests farther north, on the ground, and winters as far south as Florida and California, chiefly on saltwater.

The hooded merganser (*Lophodytes cucullatus*) is a bird of temperate zone wooded streams and ponds and nests in holes in trees. There it meets and competes with the wood duck but is easily distinguished by the big white patch in the black crest.

Condors and Vultures (*Family Cathartidae*)

Clad in funeral black as perhaps befits those attracted to dead bodies

Top: *Common merganser* (*Mergus merganser*
Bottom: *Turkey vulture* (*Cathartes aura*

the name sometimes given to vultures in Latin America is "the sanitary corps," from their role in scavenging. Vultures and the condors belong to the New World vulture family and their six species are found only in the Americas. Although related to the hawks and eagles their feet are not fitted for grasping, but the bill, with a hook at the tip, is adapted for snipping off pieces of meat and for pulling carcasses to pieces. All vultures and condors have naked heads, which may help them keep their heads clean when they are feeding on carcasses. Three species of the family occur north of Mexico.

CALIFORNIA CONDOR

The largest of the family is the California condor (*Gymnogyps californianus*), a magnificent black bird with yellow-orange head, a white patch on the underwing, and with a wingspread of 9 feet. It breeds only in the mountains northwest of Los Angeles, California, and the birds ride the thermal air currents as they soar and sail over the open lower slopes and plateaus of the interior valleys in search of their food. Dead deer, cattle and smaller animals such as rabbits and squirrels seem to provide ample food for the forty or so living birds, all that remained of this endagered species in the 1960's.

The reproduction rate of the species is low. A single egg is laid in a nest in a cave or in a jumble of rocks and it takes more than a year to raise the young. The birds breed only every other year and the young do not breed until they are six years old. But the decrease seems due to illegal shooting and perhaps poisoning of more birds each year than are produced.

BLACK AND TURKEY VULTURES

A surprising number of observers fail to distinguish between the turkey vulture (*Cathartes aura*) and the black vulture (*Coragyps atratus*). Both are black, both soar and both feed on carrion on the road and perch on fence posts, but the differences in appearance, behavior and temperament are considerable. The key identification detail at close range is the red head of the adult turkey, and the black head of the black vulture. The turkey vulture is 29 inches long and the black 25 inches long.

The turkey vulture, with its long narrow wings held above the horizontal, sails, rocks and glides over the countryside, now high, now low, with little wing motion. It searches both by sight and by scent for dead anima

62

matter. When it finds a dead rabbit for instance, it will make a solitary meal or it may have to share the carrion with a few of its fellows.

The black vulture, with relatively short, broad wings, alternately flaps and sails over the countryside. It hunts by sight, having no sense of smell, and when it finds the carcass of a cow and lands on it, other vultures that have been watching for a lead to a meal quickly arrive until the carcass is covered with a black, struggling mass of birds.

It is the black vulture that scavenges in tropical towns, patrols the waterfront and perches on roof tops; the turkey vulture is more of a country bird. Both are widespread in the southern states and the turkey vulture also ranges north in summer to the Canadian border. Sometimes turkey and black vultures perch for hours on dead trees or in treetops. But when the morning sun heats up the ground and columns of warm air rise, both species fly into them and sail lazily round and round. Whether this is simply a way of passing the time or a method for getting a good view, it is an easy way to travel, riding thermal updrafts and currents.

Both vultures sleep in tree roosts of considerable size. Both lay their eggs in a protected spot under vegetation or in a hollow log or a crevice or cave. Food is brought in the parents' gullet and regurgitated for the young.

Kites, Hawks and Eagle (*Family Accipitridae*)

A variety of birds of prey are included in the hawk family. There are the buoyant-winged kites, the short-winged hawks, the large soaring hawks, the marsh hawk, and the very large eagles. They catch living prey, vertebrate and invertebrate, in their hooked claws and tear it to pieces with the hooked bill. The nest is placed in a tree, on a cliff or on the ground, and the downy young are fed in the nest until they can fly. Most northern species make some migration and a few are long-distance migrants.

KITES

There are four kites, all with local distribution in the southern part of the country. One, the Mississippi kite, breeds only in the United States; the other three also range widely through South America to Argentina.

Cooper's Hawk (Accipiter cooperii)

Combining the shape and the aerial grace of a barn swallow with the size of a crow and the bill and feet of a hawk, the swallow-tailed kite (*Elanoides forficatus*) is elegantly clad in black and white. A bird of the southeastern states, its present headquarters is in the Everglades country of southern Florida. There it can be seen twisting and turning low over the bean fields to snatch an insect or a frog. Holding the prey in one claw, the bird dines on it in full flight. Now and then one or two birds soar up to play about the tops of nearby cypress trees. This kite is not at all shy and I have seen it dive down and snatch an insect from the foliage of a tree in Everglades City, near its nesting site in the mangroves on the edge of town. There is a curious aspect to their behavior after they breed: in July loose flocks of a hundred of them or so are occasionally seen for a brief period over the Okeechobee prairies.

Two other kites are the rare, 16-inch-long white-tailed kite (*Elanus leucurus*) of local distribution in the South and the 14-inch-long Mississippi kite (*Ictinia misisippiensis*) of the Gulf of Mexico and the lower Mississippi River area. Although their tails are square, their flight is graceful.

A fourth species, the Everglades kite (*Rostrhamus sociabilis*), 18 inches long, has broader wings and a heavier flight. The male is slaty above and below with a white base to its tail. In the United States it nests in the marshes of south Florida where its only food is the apple snail.

SHORT-WINGED HAWKS

The short-winged hawks are bird hawks and as such are not favorites of many bird lovers, sportsmen or chicken raisers. But one must admire the dash and verve of their hunting. There are three species: the small sharp-shinned (*Accipiter striatus*), the medium-sized Cooper's (*Accipiter cooperii*), and the large goshawk (*Accipiter gentilis*). In the open their flight is distinctive: alternating intervals of flapping and gliding. But these birds ordinarily are not conspicuous for they hunt by stealth and ambush, with short broad wings for bursts of speed and a long tail for sudden turns. The hungry hawk may watch from an inconspicuous perch and dart out to overtake and seize some passing bird or it may fly low over brushland, along wooded glades or through the forest and there surprise its prey. The hawk plucks its prey before tearing off pieces of flesh and swallowing them. A hawk may have a favorite plucking perch used time after time and here one can find the feathers of its victims: warbler, sparrow, robin,

Sharp-shinned hawk (Accipiter striatus)

flicker, quail or grouse. Besides being bird fanciers these hawks take other food, especially small rodents but also frogs, lizards and insects.

The sharp-shinned hawk eats small birds. The Cooper's hawk has been considered the only hawk that preys extensively on quail on southern preserves, and a winter invasion of goshawks in the New England states has been blamed for a scarcity of ruffed grouse the next year.

The loud, sharp "cac-cac-cac" that rings through the northern woods in the early spring is the goshawk's warning that an intruder is approaching its nest, a bulky structure of sticks well up in the fork of a tree. A collector who ignores the warning and climbs to the nest may regret it. Not all goshawks are aggressive, but there are records of these birds drawing blood from the shoulders and heads of egg collectors. Smaller hawks also scold intruders but are usually less bold in defending their nests.

The goshawk is 20-26 inches long, blue-gray above and finely streaked and barred below. It is a northern forest species. The Cooper's hawk, 14-20 inches long, is bluish gray above, whitish barred with red-brown below and has a rounded tail tip. It breeds over much of the United States. The sharp-shinned hawk, 10-14 inches long, is like the Cooper's hawk but smaller and has a square-tipped tail. It breeds over much of the United States and Canada. The young of the three species have brown upperparts and heavily streaked brown underparts.

SOARING HAWKS

The soaring hawks are conspicuous as large birds that perch motionless on some exposed perch, circle overhead on long, broad wings, or beat low over open country. Their prey is usually small mammals, reptiles, amphibians and insects. They do take birds, but small birds are usually alert to danger from the air and agile enough to escape these rather clumsy predators.

The thirteen species of soaring hawks are medium-sized to large birds, 16-25 inches long. While the sexes are alike except for the male being slightly smaller, there are melanistic color phases in some of the species and the young usually have a different color from the adults, presenting problems in field identification.

Rough-legged Hawk

I associate the marsh hawk (*Circus cyaneus*) of the temperate zone and the rough-legged hawk (*Buteo lagopus*) of the Arctic, for where I learned to know both species, in the salt marshes and dyked grasslands of eastern Canada, the rough-legged was the winter replacement for the summering marsh hawk. The feathered legs of the northern species seemed a logical adaptation for keeping warm, while the maked-footed marsh hawk had to go south to a warmer climate for the winter. The roughleg is a heavier bird with broader wings and spends more of his time perched on fence posts and on trees. But it also beats over the grasslands and often hovers in the air over one spot where it hopes that a mouse will appear.

The summer home of the rough-legged hawk is the Arctic barrens where lemmings provide its main food. There the hawk selcts some high point such as a boulder, cliff edge or shelf on a steep river bank, or, if in the edge of timber, a treetop for its nest. The same nest may be used year after year and the accumulation of droppings and debris below it will cause special lichens to grow there luxuriantly enough to merit the name "bird garden."

The bird is 21 inches long, a brownish and buffy bird with a blackish belly and a white base to its tail. In a melanistic phase, the head and body are mostly black.

On the western plains lives the related 24-inch-long ferruginous hawk (*Buteo regalis*) whose main food is rodents.

Red-tailed Hawk

The fork of a leafy tree in a woodlot near a New England farm, a cabbage palm on a Florida prairie, a ledge on a cutbank above a western river, or a giant cactus in the Southwest all furnish sites for the bulky nest of the red-tailed hawk (*Buteo jamaicensis*). These indicate the great variety of habitats in which this species lives across the continent. The northern birds withdraw southward in winter but return early in the spring, when their loud "Kreee," uttered as the bird circles over a woodlot, announces their arrival on their breeding grounds.

The redtail is one of the larger hawks, 22 inches long; the red-brown tail and the white underparts with a band of dark streaks across the abdomen identify the adult. In the immature the tail is brown barred black and the underparts extensively streaked.

The related Harlan's hawk (*Buteo harlani*), breeding in Alaska and wintering in the Missouri-Texas area, is a very variable species, and some suggest that it is a local variant of the redtail.

Swainson's Hawk

The commonest hawk of the western plains is the Swainson's hawk (*Buteo swainsoni*). It seeks its prey by soaring and gliding, following a tractor-drawn gang-ploy for the sake of the mice turned out of their homes and by perching near a ground squirrel burrow and waiting for the squirrel to emerge. The hawk may also fly through swarms of insects, seizing them in its feet and eating them on the wing, and it may land where grasshoppers are common and catch and eat them on the ground.

The Swainson's hawk prefers a nest in a tree along a watercourse, though even a low bush may suffice, especially if it has a commanding view. While the other two hawks of the plains, the red-tailed and the ferruginous, are permanent residents, withdrawing somewhat in winter, most of the Swainson's hawks go to South America for the winter, traveling both spring and autumn in great flocks of thousands of birds. In its pale phase, the

Both: Red-tailed hawks (Buteo jamaicensis)

Swainson's hawk has white underparts with a brownish band across the breast. This hawk is 20 inches long.

Other Soaring Hawks

In the eastern part of the United States within the range of the redtail are three smaller species. One is the red-shouldered hawk (*Buteo lineatus*), 20 inches long, that lives in damper woods and specializes in eating frogs and snakes. The second is the broad-winged hawk (*Buteo platypterus*), 16 inches long, a less conspicuous soaring bird. The third is the short-tailed hawk (*Buteo brachyurus*), 17 inches long, a tropical species that enters the United States only in Florida.

There are five other soaring hawks, 17-23 inches long, that range north-ward from Central America only into the Mexican border country of the United States. These are: the zone-tailed hawk (*Buteo albonotatus*) of wooded canyons; the white-tailed hawk (*Buteo albicaudatus*), common in the edge of the deserts and grasslands; the gray hawk (*Buteo nitidus*) of mesquite shrubbery and cottonwood along watercourses; the Harris' hawk (*Parabuteo unicinctus*) of mesquite and brushland; and the black hawk (*Buteogallus anthracinus*) of trees along watercourses.

Marsh Hawk

One October day when prowling a duck marsh I flushed a marsh hawk (*Circus cyaneus*) from the carcass of a black duck on which it had just started to dine. I thought that this was evidence that marsh hawks kill ducks, but when I examined the carcass I found a gunshot wound. Obviously the hawk was cleaning up after a wildfowler.

Marshes and grasslands, northern ones in summer, southern ones in winter, are the haunts of the marsh hawks. Both the 19-inch silvery male and the 22-inch brown female have a white rump. The flight of these slender, long-winged, long-tailed birds is also distinctive: buoyant and often gliding on wings angled upward in shallow V's. The marsh hawk beats back and forth over meadow and marsh grass. A sudden check, turn and dive into the grass and it disappears for a few moments, eating its prey of mice and rats on the spot. The nest is built on the ground among grass or bushes, and the five eggs are white, and may have brownish markings.

EAGLES

The eagle has long been a symbol of strength and courage, and so the

Left: Bald eagle (Haliaeetus leucocephalus)
Right: Golden eagle (Aquila chrysaetos)

bald eagle (*Haliaeetus leucocephalus*), found only on the American continent, was chosen by congress in 1782 as our national bird. Sitting motionless by the hour on some commanding lookout or soaring overhead on
broad wings, white-headed, white-tailed, and three feet long, the bald
eagle is a magnificent bird. Its nearest relatives are the fishing and sea
eagles of the Old World. Correlated with its dependence on fish, the bald
eagle's main habitat is near water, especially larger rivers, lakes and the
sea. Its distribution thus was always local but its numbers have decreased
in recent years and it is common now only on the Alaska and the Florida
coasts.

In its fishing the bald eagle may watch from a perch or fly over the
water until a fish comes close enough to the surface to be seized. Probably
nowhere were eagles more abundant than along the north Pacific coast,
where herring and salmon provided much of its food. Congregations of as
many as 300 birds were seen there in the past. Dead fish washed up in the
shallows are also eaten; the eagle will even rob the osprey of its prey,
or upon occasion take waterfowl from the surface of the water.

The bald eagle's huge bulky nest of sticks is built high in the fork
of a tree and is added to year after year until it may be 20 feet deep and
9 feet across. Two white eggs are laid, both parents share nest duties, and

71

Marsh hawk (*Circus cyaneus*)

the young in all-black plumage fly at about thirteen weeks. After four or five years the bird acquires the adult white head and white tail.

Unlike the bald eagle, the golden eagle (*Aquila chrysaetos*) is a bird of the mountains, mesas and arid plains of wilderness areas. Its staple food is small mammals such as rabbits, ground squirrels and marmots. The adult golden eagle, 33-38 inches long, is dark brown except for a golden crown and nape.

Osprey (*Family Pandionidae*)

Because of anatomical peculiarities, the osprey (*Pandion haliaetus*), a fish hawk with a nearly world-wide distribution, is classified in a family by itself. When their favorite food is scarce, most birds turn to something else. But the osprey's diet is almost exclusively fish, and fresh fish at that. In foraging, the osprey flies along some distance above the water, now flapping now sailing, hovering here and there for a moment until a fish is sighted. Then on half-closed wings it plunges with talons extended, splashing into the water, and emerging to fly off with the fish in its claws.

The osprey's nest is a bulky one of sticks and trash. It can be found in a variety of locations. Sometimes the osprey's nest is solitary on some high tree, far from the water. By Florida lakes loose colonies may occupy the fringing cypress trees. In some places along the Atlantic coast ospreys nest near dwellings, and on islands they can be found on the ground.

The osprey, 22 inches long, is brown above with a white nape and white below. In flight the long, rather narrow wings show a distinctive angled bend.

Falcons and Caracaras *(Family Falconidae)*

Structural characters, not appearance, cause the falcons and caracaras to be grouped in one family. The falcons have pointed wings, swift flight, hooked bills and claws and catch their own prey, often other birds. The family is world-wide and there are six American species. They nest on cliff ledges, in trees and holes in trees and both parents help feed the downy young there. The caracaras in tropical America are scavengers and insect-eaters. Only one species reaches the United States.

PEREGRINE FALCON

Once on the high plains of Colorado I saw a blue-wing teal dart across a slough at top speed and suddenly realized that fifty yards behind it was a peregrine falcon *(Falco peregrinus)*. The falcon rapidly overtook and seized the teal, and together the two birds came to earth. This is the falcon prized by falconers for its speed and courage when flown at game. Sometimes the falcon, instead of grappling with its prey from behind, stoops from above and knocks it senseless and then turns and follows it to earth to pluck and make a meal of it.

The peregrine falcon's distribution is nearly world-wide. In America it nests on the Arctic islands and south to California and Georgia, usually selecting a cliff ledge for a nest site. This bird's food is almost entirely other birds taken on the wing. In migration the falcon may follow the sea coast, feeding on migrating shore birds, and may winter near areas of wintering waterfowl. A few peregrine falcons take up winter quarters in cities where they feed on the abundant pigeons, and the peregrine falcon sometimes even nests on the ledges of skyscrapers, substituting them for natural cliffs.

About the size of a crow, 17-19 inches long, the adult is slaty above, with black crown and bar across the white face. The underparts are whitish, lightly barred and spotted. The brownish immature are heavily streaked below.

SPARROW HAWK AND OTHER FALCONS

Such phrases as "the prettiest and jauntiest of our hawks" and "the most light-hearted and frolicsome," applied to the sparrow hawk *(Falco sparverius)* by earlier ornithologists, characterize vividly our commonest and smallest falcon. The red-brown back, black face marks and small size, about 11 inches long, make identification easy. It lives across the continent in open country and the edge of woodlands and perches on stub, post or wire watching for its prey. Often it varies this routine by flying and soaring over the fields, pausing every now and then to hover in one place to scan the ground and then dropping down to take a grasshopper or mouse. "Sparrow hawk" is a misnomer, though occasionally it does take small birds from the ground; "grasshopper falcon" would be more appropriate and "killy hawk," a folk name derived from its call, has a certain charm. The sparrow hawk has a surprising trait of flying above and diving at other large birds, even red-tailed hawks and eagles, as though in play.

Unlike most falcons, the sparrow hawk nests in a hole in a tree, often in the site of an old flicker nest. The three to seven eggs are whitish to lavender, handsomely marked with brown. The parent tears off pieces of meat for the chicks to take from her beak, but later the mouse or bird is left for the young to devour by themselves.

There are four other falcons in America. The large gyrfalcon *(Falco rusticolus)*, 20-25 inches long and ranging in color from nearly white to nearly black, lives in the Arctic, rarely coming south of northern Canada. The prairie falcon *(Falco mexicanus)* of the dry western plains and mountains is a pale, browner version of the peregrine falcon. The pigeon hawk *(Falco columbarius)*, 12 inches long, is a dark, northern tree-nesting species wintering south to Mexico The aplomado falcon *(Falco femoralis)*,

Osprey (Pandion haliaetus)

17 inches long, is a more southern species that ranges north to the Mexican border country.

CARACARA

Though sometimes called the Mexican eagle, the caracara (*Caracara cheriway*) is most unusual looking and recalls no other bird except perhaps an oversized, scrawny hen. It walks about in grasslands catching grasshoppers in its bill, perches on roadside fence posts, and feeds on rabbits and raccoons killed by automobiles. In south Florida it nests in the cabbage palms of the prairies. Its flight, on broad wings, is swift and direct. The caracara, 22 inches long, is mostly black with a red face, white cheeks and throat, and a black and white breast. A tropical species, it enters the United States in south Florida, Texas and Arizona.

Chachalacas (*Family Cracidae*)

In the South and Central American forests lives a family of fowl-like birds variously called guans, curassows and chachalacas, of which one, the chachalaca (*Ortalis vetula*), ranges north into the forests and brushlands of the lower Rio Grande Valley. These birds are somewhat pheasant-like in size and shape but have long broad tails rounded at the tip. In Central America they live in the upper branches of woodland trees, occasionally giving the loud, ringing, several-syllabled calls that have given them their name, often shortened to "chacha." Their nest of twigs is placed in the fork of a tree but the young are down covered, active and soon able to follow their parents. The chacha's food is fruit and berries and the birds sometimes come to the ground to feed. The chachalaca, 22 inches long, is unpatterned brownish above and below.

Ptarmigan and Grouse (*Family Tetraonidae*)

Ten of the eighteen species of the grouse family live in North America, some on the tundra, others in the northern woodlands and still others in the temperate grasslands. They are plump-breasted, with short, rounded wings and intricately patterned colors that blend with their habitat. The food of these birds consists of a wide variety of plant material and changes with the season, with a few insects added in the summer. The mating pattern varies greatly from monogamous mating to a complicated social organization of males on large community dance grounds where the females come for courting. The nest is a scantily lined hollow on the ground; the down-clad young follow the female and can fly at a very early age. The female often uses a broken-wing ruse, feigning injury to lure predators from the nest or the young.

RUFFED GROUSE

Wherever there are hardwood trees in the northern forests a common sound in spring is the drumming of the ruffed grouse (*Bonasa umbellus*). On a fallen log the cock bird struts, tail raised and spread fan-wise, wings drooping, and black ruff spread. Soon he stands upright and beats the air with his wings, slowly at first, "thump-thump—" and then quickening to blend into a roll. This announces to other males that the site is occupied and to females that a mating station is at hand. When a female arrives, the male struts again with much shaking of head and ruff, and mating takes place. No pairs are formed and the female goes her solitary way to make her nest, incubate her eggs and lead away her brood of tiny chicks, which may stay together in a loose flock for some time.

On snowy winter mornings parties of half a dozen grouse may be seen silhouetted against the sky as the birds perch on the outer branches of birch and aspen eating their staple winter food of buds and twigs. With the coming of spring the grouse, now solitary, walks with quick firm steps along forest glade or margin, picking a green leaf here, a bud, flower or insect there. With the ripening of berries and later of nuts, these are added to the diet. Old buckwheat fields and orchards adjoining woodlots are also favorite feeding places in the autumn.

The ruffed grouse can fly silently, but very often a bird bursts into flight from almost underfoot and with a roar of wings disappears into the forest. Sometimes, so the "partridge hunters" claim, the bird dodges behind a tree trunk in its flight. Occasionally a ruffed grouse appears in a most unlikely place far from its natural habitat, including even a city. Once I saw one in a duck marsh; strays have been called crazy grouse.

78

Top: Sage grouse (*Centrocercus urophasianus*)
Bottom: White-tailed ptarmigan (*Lagopus leucurus*)

The ruffed grouse. 17-19 inches long, has a gray and a red-brown color phase and is easily recognized by its broad, barred, fanlike tail. The bird's range is across the northern part of the continent.

SAGE GROUSE

My first meeting with the sage grouse (*Centrocercus urophasianus*) was in Alberta when five birds, seeming unbelievably large, walked across a mesa road in front of me. Shortly after, in a nearby sagebrush flat, a flock of ten flushed from almost underfoot and I was surprised that they could have remained hidden for so long. In these sagebrush flats, which provide both food and cover, flocks of hundreds of sage grouse gather to spend the winter.

The communal display and mating of the sage grouse is the most complex and spectacular of any of our grouse. The cock birds spread and erect their long, pointed tail feathers, inflate their throat sacs and dance on a display ground where scores or even hundreds of males have assembled. Here the females come only to mate and then go off to nest and rear the young by themselves.

The sage grouse is a gray-brown bird with a black belly. The male, our largest grouse, is 28 inches long and may weigh as much as 8 pounds. The female is one-third smaller. The range of the species is in the sagebrush of the arid plains and basins of the West.

PTARMIGAN

The three ptarmigan in North America are birds of arctic and alpine tundra. They moult from a white winter plumage to a brownish summer coat and back again so that they match the prevailing color of their environment. Only the wings are white all year. The feet and toes are heavily feathered and the birds dig into the snow to sleep sheltered from the cold. Unlike most grouse, the willow ptarmigan pairs and the male guards the nest and accompanies the female and the young.

The smallest species, the 13-inch white-tailed ptarmigan (*Lagopus leucurus*), lives on the alpine tundra of the western mountains from Alaska to isolated peaks in Colorado and New Mexico. It is the only ptarmigan with a white tail summer and winter. In summer in the Mackenzie Mountains I found the solitary males high among the rocky peaks while the females with their broods of five to six small young were

Top: *Ruffed grouse* (Bonasa umbellus)
Bottom: *Chachalaca* (Ortalis vetula)

at lower altitudes in the grassy tundra meadows near timberline, where living conditions were easier. Even small young were feeding on leaves and berries. Evidently other small vertical migrations are performed for I was told that during severe winter weather, when the snow is deep and the birds are all white, they gather in the valleys and feed on the buds and twigs of willows projecting above the snow.

The rock ptarmigan (*Lagopus mutus*) is a bird of the high Arctic, living in rocky exposed situations in the northern barrens and northwestern mountains. In summer plumage it is a gray brown while in winter it is white, although there is a black patch in front of the eye and the tail is black in all seasons. The willow ptarmigan (*Lagopus lagopus*), the largest ptarmigan species, is 16 inches long and in summer is red-brown. This is the common ptarmigan of the open barrens. In winter the birds gather in great flocks and some fly southward as far as central Canada where the buds and twigs of birch, willow and alder appear more plentifully above the snow.

OTHER GROUSE

The blue grouse (*Dendragapus obscurus*) and the spruce grouse (*Canachites canadensis*) are dark birds with dark gray and black in the plumage, though the females are browner. Both species are associated with coniferous trees whose needles are their staple food in winter. The blue grouse, 17-21 inches long, lives in the coniferous forests of the humid Pacific coast and the western mountains. The range of the 16-inch-long spruce grouse is the northern forests across the continent. This grouse has been called the "fool hen" because of its tameness and I have seen it snared with a bootlace noose on the end of a switch.

The greater prairie chicken (*Tympanuchus cupido*) and the sharp-tailed grouse (*Pedioecetes phasianellus*) are buffy brown birds of the brushlands and grasslands of the interior of the continent. The former is more southern, the latter more northern, but there is a broad overlap in their ranges. In both species the males gather to display, fight and mate with the females that come to the courting grounds. The greater prairie chicken ranges from central Alberta to eastern Texas. It is 16-18 inches long with a short rounded black tail, regularly barred underparts and an elongated tuft of neck feathers just above the inflatable throat sacs displayed in courting. A related species, the lesser prairie chicken (*Tympanuchus palli*

Blue grouse (Dendragapus obscurus)

licinctus), lives in the southwestern Great Plains. The more northern sharp-tailed grouse, 15-20 inches long, lives from Alaska to James Bay and south to northern New Mexico. It is 15-20 inches long with a pointed, partly white tail, V-shaped markings in its underparts and inflatable purplish air sacs on the sides of the neck.

Quail, Partridge and Pheasants

(Family Phasianidae)

The headquarters of the pheasant family, which also includes the domestic fowl and the peacock, is southern Asia. Three species have been introduced from Eurasia and naturalized as game birds in America; the ring-necked

pheasant, the gray partridge and the chukar. There is also a very distinct group of American quail that have evolved in the New World, the bobwhite and its relatives. All these birds nest on the ground and have downy young that follow the parent. Their diet is seeds, succulent vegetable matter and some insects.

AMERICAN QUAIL

There are six species of quail in the United States: the bobwhite (*Colinus virginianus*) in the eastern half and the five others in the Southwest or the Far West, in mixed open country and brushlands. They are small, short-tailed, plump birds, 9-11 inches long, with rounded wings. They do their foraging on the ground. Winter coveys are formed and when these break up pairs are formed which endure until the young are well grown.

Bobwhite

Although I have shot quail on a big plantation in the Deep South where they were abundant I would resent anyone molesting the covey of a dozen quail that walk across our Florida dooryard twice a day for the scratch feed put out for them. For me the quail has changed from a game bird to a song bird. In the spring, male birds whistle their name, "bob-white" or "bob bob-white," telling the world they are unmated. A female joins a male, a pair is formed, and both sexes share nest duties and accompany the downy young, whose wings grow quickly so that they can fly while still very small. Like some grouse, the bobwhite, especially the male, may feign a broken wing and, fluttering and limping, may try to lure a predator to follow it away from the hidden young.

The winter bobwhite, in coveys of one or two dozen birds, ranges on foot over wide areas of grass and weedy country among thickets, shrubbery and open stands of trees. When danger approaches, the birds crouch, invisible, until they all fly up with bombshell suddenness and scatter. Later they give location calls and reassemble. At night in some dense cover the covey forms a circle on the ground and the birds sleep with heads pointing outward so that at least one head will point toward any approaching danger.

The bobwhite, widespread in the eastern half of the country and south into Mexico, is a red-brown bird, 10 inches long, the male with a white throat and eyebrow stripe; the female is similar but duller in coloring.

Top: *White-tailed ptarmigan* (*Lagopus leucurus*)
Bottom: *Spruce grouse* (*Canachites canadensis*)

California Quail

With the black curved plume of its forehead nodding in time with its quick short steps as it forages over suburban lawns or in city parks or in the country, the California quail (*Lophortyx californicus*) is a familiar bird of the Far West. Its habitat needs are: open ground over which to forage; shrubbery into which to retreat for safety; and trees or tall shrubbery in which to roost and sleep. The California quail can do without drinking water, but only if there is enough succulent vegetation in its food to provide the water needs of its body.

The winter coveys break up and pairs are formed to the accompaniment of fighting and loud, three-syllable calls. Later the male often perches sentry-like in a shrub or tree while the female incubates; he also helps guard the young. When the young are grown, families merge to form large coveys. This quail is a 10-inch-long, blue, gray and brown bird with a frontal plume that curls forward over the bill, white-streaked flanks and a scaled pattern on the abdomen. Its range is the lowlands of the Far West from Washington State to Mexico.

Other Southwestern Quail

The Gambel's quail (*Lophortyx gambelii*) of the shrub deserts of the Southwest differs from the California quail in having the abdomen white with or without a black patch. In the brushy clearings of the mountain forests of the Far West from Washington State to California lives the mountain quail (*Oreortyx pictus*), with a long straight head plume and white-barred flanks. In the mesa and pine-oak country of the desert mountains in Mexico and north in the area from Arizona to west Texas lives the Harlequin quail (*Cyrtonyx montezumae*). It has a short, full crest, a complex black and white face pattern and dark flanks spotted with white. On the desert and scrub grasslands of Mexico and the Arizona–Colorado–west Texas area lives the scaled quail (*Callipepla squamata*). It has much scaled blue-gray in its plumage and a short upright crest tipped with white which has given it the name of "cottontop."

INTRODUCED PHEASANTS AND PARTRIDGE

Of the many game birds introduced into America by sportsmen to supplement native species, especially in habitats newly created by man's activities, only three species have been successful: the ring-necked pheasant (*Phas-

86

Top: Greater prairie chickens (Tympanuchus cupido)
Bottom: California quail (Lophortyx californicus)

Gambel's quail (Lophortyx gambelii)

ianus colchicus) of China, the gray partridge or Hungarian partridge (*Perdix perdix*) of Europe, and the Chukar or rock partridge (*Alectoris graeca*) of southern Asia.

In the autumn the hunter finds the ring-necked pheasant a solitary bird adept at skulking, hiding and running through weedy tangles and brush. When finally forced to fly it rises with cackling notes and roaring wings to fly low into cover and then run again. In the winter some country people put out corn and have groups of colorful, long-tailed males and brown females visit their yard. The casual traveler may see the birds along country roadsides. Cock pheasants patrol the boundaries of their spring territories and announce their presence by periodically crowing and flapping their wings. In displaying to a female a cock bird partly spreads one wing, spreads his tail and tilts it toward the female and walks around her with lowered head. The female scratches out a hollow for her nest, and incubates her brood.

The pheasant has been very successful in a broad band of grass and farmland across the central part of the continent, but especially so in the farmlands of the eastern part of the northern Great Plains; there it eats many insects, even though its main diet is seeds and grain. The male is 3 feet long and has a very long, pointed tail, much bright red-brown in its plumage, a green head and neck and a white neckring. The smaller female is generally buffy brown.

The gray partridge or Hungarian partridge has been nearly as successful a colonist as the pheasant, especially in the open dry grassland of the northern plains and in the vicinity of irrigated land of northern scrub desert regions. Locally it has succeeded on farmlands in the Northeast. The coveys of one to three dozen birds feed in open fields, run when disturbed and then fly as a flock to a distant field. The birds pair in the spring and the nest is hidden in last year's dead grass. The gray partridge, 13 inches long, is gray-brown in color with a chestnut patch on its breast and a short chestnut tail.

The chukar or rock partridge has been successfully established in desert mountain areas of the western United States, living in the sagebrush country on rocky slopes where vegetation is scant. This partridge is about 14 inches long, a gray and brown bird with a white throat outlined in black, reddish legs and prominent black bars on white flanks.

Turkey (*Family Meleagrididae*)

It was by Fish-eating Creek in south Florida that I came upon my first wild turkeys—a band of five. Two were sprawled on their breasts on a sandbar, two were walking along the water's edge picking at the sand, and one was reaching up to the seed heads of a clump of giant grass. I had but a moment to admire them before they disappeared on foot like swift shadows among the cypress trunks. These were the most magnificent, impressive birds I had ever seen. They represented not large cousins of the grouse and quail, but compatriots of deer, cougar and Indians that hunted or were hunted when the creek was called *Tholothlopopka-Hatchee*.

The gobbler (*Meleagris gallopavo*) with fan-shaped tail raised, wings drooping, and red wattles inflated, gobbles and struts as part of the mating display that gathers a number of hens about him as a harem for a brief period in the spring. Then the hens separate to carry out the rest of the reproduction cycle. The nest, a hollow on the ground, receives from eight to fourteen eggs, and the downy young follow the mother and fly when two weeks old. Then, like the adults, they roost in trees and spend the day walking about in the grassy deciduous and southern pine forests, feeding on seeds, berries and some insects. Although the adults fly well, they often prefer to run to escape danger.

The turkey's present range in the eastern and southern United States is much fragmented, but the birds are increasing in numbers thanks to people interested in saving our wildlife. A few years ago, in two hours on the roads and trails of a Florida state park I saw twenty-four turkeys under wilderness conditions; I also saw seven deer, an otter and a wildcat, demonstrating that we can retain some of our heritage, unchanged.

The male turkey grows up to 4 feet in length and 35 pounds in weight; the female is smaller. The only other species in the turkey family is the ocellated turkey (*Agriocharis ocellata*) of Central America and Mexico.

Cranes (*Family Gruidae*)

One of the attractions of living in the flatwoods of south Florida is to wake at first light while the great horned owls are still hooting and hear the musical trumpeting of a pair of sandhill cranes (*Grus canadensis*) in a nearby wet bushy flat. But the open prairies and pastures are better places to watch the cranes. There the pairs and small parties walk about bent over, poking, pecking, and grubbing for seeds, green leaves, roots and insects. Alarmed, the cranes stand up tall and straight and then with long running steps and slow beats of their long broad wings, with necks extended and legs trailing, they fly to a distance, or circle and soar on motionless wings until lost to sight.

The dance of the cranes is seen all year, but especially at nesting time. A pair or several birds bow, bob, dance and hop with partly spread wings

Each pair then seeks a secluded shallow pond where vegetation is heaped into a small island with a hollow on top for the two eggs. The downy young soon follow their parents and at first take morsels of food from the parent's bill. It is not long until they can feed themselves, and in about two months they can fly. The family group may join others. The Florida sandhill cranes are non-migratory and few in number. There are other, scattered populations of sandhill cranes in the western and central part of the country that are migratory, but the long-range migrants nest on the Arctic tundra. There the family parties gather into large flocks on the Arctic river flats and in September move southward in flocks of scores and hundreds. The size and numbers of these birds, their flight formations, and the musical trumpet-like calls that come clearly to earth when the lines of birds are but specks in the sky, make these migrations spectacular. One of the famous stopping places is on the flats of the Platte River in Nebraska where one flock on a sandbar was estimated to contain 100,000 birds standing shoulder to shoulder and covering a band four yards wide and half a mile long. The autumn goal of these birds is the flat open country of California, New Mexico, Texas and Mexico where flocks of thousands sleep standing in the ankle-deep water of shallow lakes and on river bars and fly out to feed on grain fields and pastures as much as twelve miles away.

The sandhill crane is a gray bird with a bare red crown and stands about 4 feet high, has a straight blunt bill and flies with neck outstretched.

The whooping crane (*Grus americana*) is larger, standing about 5 feet high, and is all white with small black wing tips. Like the trumpeter swan, it used to nest in ponds in what is now ranch and farmland. In 1955 there were only 21 living birds. Since then the species has increased very slowly and in 1968 there were about 50 birds. All of them summer in the muskeg country of Wood Buffalo Park on the Alberta—Mackenzie border, and all spend the winter on the Aransas Wildlife Refuge of coastal Texas. On the danger list of vanishing species, they are rigorously protected.

Limpkin (*Family Aramidae*)

The limpkin (*Aramus guarauna*), 28 inches long, is a brown, white-streaked bird recalling an oversized rail or a diminutive crane. Actually the limpkin family, with but a single species, is a link between the cranes and the rails. It is mostly tropical American in distribution but ranges north to Florida and adjacent Georgia.

Its habitat is the grassy marshes and the edges of wooded streams where it walks about on the banks and in the water looking for the large snails and mussels that form its main food. Litters of empty shells mark its feeding places. Though of local distribution, there is one place I have always been able to find it: by cypress-fringed Wachulla Springs near the little dock from which one leaves to see the dancing catfish.

The species is said to walk with a limp and have a wailing cry. The nest is built among grass stalks or brushy tangles, four to eight brown spotted eggs are laid, and the downy young leave the nest soon after hatching.

Rails *(Family Rallidae)*

Most rails are shy retiring birds of the marshes, where they walk about in the shelter of dense grasses and reeds and are more often heard than seen. America has six of these, from 5 to 17 inches long. There are also two gallinules and a coot that measure from 12 to 16 inches long. They are less shy and retiring and swim in open water. The nests are placed low in the vegetation; 5 to 12 speckled, whitish to olive or buff eggs are laid in them, and the downy chicks, which are black, soon accompany the parents. Northern populations winter from our warmer states southward.

MARSH RAILS

The salt marshes that fringe the coasts southward from San Francisco on the Pacific, and New York on the Atlantic, are the favorite habitats of the clapper rail *(Rallus longirostris)*. Much of the bird's life is spent out of sight in the marsh grass. Sometimes a startled bird gives a series of rapidly repeated calls: a harsh, cackling "kek —." Others take it up and the calls fly over the marsh. But the birds do come out on exposed mud, walking slowly and daintily, with head going back and forth and short tail twitching in time with its steps. Startled, the bird runs with its body and neck stretched out and its tail straight up, and disappears into cover. Sometimes clapper rails swim across narrow channels and feed on the open mud along with sandpipers, picking up crustaceans, insects, small fish and seeds.

King rail (Rallus elegans)

The nest of grass and sedge is built up above the mud so that ordinary tides do not flood it, and is sometimes hidden from above by the grasses arching overhead. Here about a dozen eggs are laid. The downy black chicks accompany the parent, at least at first, even swimming across narrow channels with them, and the young quickly learn to pick up their own food.

The clapper rail, 15 inches long, has a grayish or olive brown-streaked back, pinkish gray neck and breast, and black and white barred flanks. There is some southward movement of northern birds but this rail is a permanent resident over much of its range.

The king rail (*Rallus elegans*), 17 inches long, is similar to the clapper rail but much more reddish brown and it lives in freshwater marshes of the eastern half of the country. The related Virginia rail (*Rallus limicola*), breeding across the central part of the continent in marshes, is similar to the king rail but much smaller, measuring only 10 inches long.

The one rail I have been able to watch regularly is the sora (*Porzana carolina*). When spring high water floods the dense fringing vegetation of small ponds near Chicago the soras walk in the open over the floating water plants in the evenings. They keep their heads down and tails up and twitching as they take slow, cautious steps while searching for tiny insects and choice bits of green plants. Sometimes a water weed to which a bird trusts its weight sinks and the bird flutters to a safer perch; sometimes it climbs into the branches of a buttonwood bush that dips into the water. Always the soras are near dense vegetation to which they half run, half fly, when alarmed. Though this might imply limited powers of flight, the sora that nests in marshes across the northern part of the United States and adjacent Canada is a long-distance migrant, and while some winter in our southern states, others fly as far as Peru. The sora, 9 inches long, has brown, streaked upperparts, black and white barred flanks, and in adult plumage has a black patch around the bill.

There are two other marsh rails in America. The black rail (*Laterallus jamaicensis*), 5½ inches long, is a blackish brown and slaty bird with small white markings on the upperparts. It is one of the shyest, most rarely seen of the rails. The yellow rail (*Coturnicops noveboracensis*), 7 inches long, with much light brown and buffy in its plumage, is another species that is rarely seen.

GALLINULES AND COOTS

The gallinules are large rails with little pattern in their plumage, naked frontal shields and long slender toes. They walk over floating vegetation and among the reeds but spend much of their time swimming, being less retiring than most rails. The coots are still more aquatic and less retiring than the gallinules; they have lobed toes to aid in swimming and spend much time on open water. There are two species of gallinules and one of coots in the United States.

In the spring some American coots (*Fulica americana*) break their northward journey on our Midwestern ponds. Their clownish chicken-turned-duck appearance makes them worth watching. No one should mistake a swimming coot for a duck; the humped back, thick neck and down-tilted bill are quite different and the coot's bobbing head goes back and forth, keeping time with his swimming feet. Sometimes in diving head first in shallow water a coot pops back up tail first, dragging a strand of water weed to eat. Mating activities are begun in various ways. A coot lowers its head and swims at another, which skitters away with a pattering of feet, or ad-

Top: Sora rail (*Porzana carolina*)
Bottom: American coot (*Fulica americana*)

vances when the attacker turns and spreads its raised tail to show its white undertail and swims away, or the two birds may grapple with their fee while flapping their wings and pecking at each other. Then, breaking off they swim to an old muskrat home, walk out, and stand, like grotesque chickens, preening.

How different are the great winter congregations of coots, flocks number ing in the hundreds, if not thousands, on the shallow lakes of the South There they seem only to feed and rest. When the flock is disturbed there i a great pattering of many feet as the birds laboriously get under way to fly a few hundred yards and flop into the water again. On their nesting ground the birds favor marsh-fringed ponds where they pair to the acompanimen of clucks, grunts and cackles, make a nest among the reeds and raise down black young that swim along with their parents.

The coot, 15 inches long, is slaty gray with a black head and neck and a white bill and nests widely on ponds and marshes in the northeast, centra and western parts of the country.

The common gallinule (*Gallinula chloropus*) nests throughout the eastern half of the United States, and occasionally in the West. One sum mer the high point of our gallinule-watching at a cattail pond was seeing a parent, presumably the female, settle her brood for the night. She swam to a platform of dead reeds with three of her chicks, but four others swam and climbed about and only after much fidgeting and clucking did the straggle onto the platform and snuggle down by the female. By this time the first arrivals had become restless and were out on little excursions o their own. And so it went, until nearly dark when all were huddled abou the female.

Only a single pair of these rather slender, dainty birds lived on this pond and they obviously had made a nest hidden in the reeds. Usually one o another of the birds was to be seen swimming near the cattails, pecking a the waterweed or walking over a raft of cattail stems, and adding its cluck ing to the chorus of grebe, frog and blackbird voices.

The common gallinule, 13 inches long, has a red-fronted shield and slaty gray plumage with a white flank stripe. The related purple gallinul (*Porphyrula martinica*) is a more colorful bird with much green and purple blue in its plumage. It breeds only in the southeastern states and southwar and seems to spend more time walking about on floating vegetation tha does the common gallinule.

American oystercatcher (Haematopus palliatus)

Jacanas (*Family Jacanidae*)

The very long toes and toenails of the jacana (*Jacana spinosa*) enable it t
stand, walk and run over the lily pads and floating aquatic vegetation tha
chokes tropical backwaters, lagoons and marshy pools. Scorning conceal
ment, the bird feeds in the open and even calls attention to itself by raisin
and fluttering its conspicuous rufous and yellow wings. The jacana, a dis
tant relative of the plovers, is 9 inches long, has a black head and neck
rufous body and rufous and yellow wings. It is a tropical American specie
and ranges northward only to southeastern Texas, where it is of casua
occurrence.

Oystercatchers (*Family Haematopodidae*)

Black or black and white shorebirds as big as crows and with long, red bill
the oystercatchers are unmistakable. Like many of their smaller sandpipe
and plover relatives the oystercatchers are birds of the sea's edge and see
their food in the intertidal zone. The long red bill is especially adapte
for feeding on shellfish by being compressed and square-tipped like a screw
driver; it serves as an oyster knife for opening and cracking shellfish. Th
birds go in small flocks in the winter, form pairs in the spring, and lay thei
two or three eggs in hollows in the sand or on rock above tidal level. Th
downy young, patterned and colored for camouflage as are the eggs, soo
follow their parents. At the approach of danger the chicks crouch motior
less while the adults circle about, uttering a loud, emphatic "wheep—".

The American oystercatcher (*Haematopus palliatus*), 17 inches long, is
black and white, shy and uncommon bird of the sand beaches of the soutl
eastern states; numbers of them winter on the Carolina coasts. The bir
feed on the ebbing tide, following the receding water and flying out t
oyster bards as they become exposed. They wade out to surprise the littl
raccoon oysters before they close their shells, not to mention picking up c
probing for other invertebrates. They nest on the broad sand beache

The black oystercatcher (*Haematopus bachmani*), 17 inches long and wit
an all black plumage, is a permanent resident of the rocky coasts, where th
surf pounds, from California to the Aleutian Islands. It is a tamer, le

active bird than its Atlantic counterpart and favors rocky offshore islets for nesting. Among the marine invertebrates it eats are limpets and barnacles that it chisels off the rocks.

Plovers (*Family Charadriidae*)

The shorebirds form a large group that includes five families: the plover, sandpiper, oystercatcher, stilt and phalarope, of which the sandpiper and the plover are best known. The American members of the plover family are grouped as ring-necked plovers; killdeer and mountain plovers; black-bellied and golden plovers; and surfbirds and turnstones. All these birds nest on the ground and usually lay four heavily spotted eggs, though some southern species may lay only two. The downy young follow the parents from the time of hatching.

RING-NECKED PLOVERS

The four ring-necked plovers, about 6-7½ inches long, often associate with the many small sandpipers of similar size on beaches and mudflats, but are easily recognized by the black neck-band. Their profile and behavior differ too. They have bigger heads and shorter necks, and while they may fly in small flocks they tend to scatter when feeding. Each runs a few steps, stops, bends over to peck at the sand, straightens up and repeats the process. By contrast sandipipers tend to remain in flocks and to be bent over, industriously probing the sand as they walk or run along. A plover's voice is distinctive: two or three whistled, melodious motes. All four ring-necked plovers nest on the sand or ground of open expanses of beaches or bare flats.

The semipalmated plover (*Charadrius semipalmatus*), with a brown back and orange-yellow legs, nests in the low Arctic barrens and migrates through the interior and along both coasts to winter from the southern states southward. The piping plover (*Charadrius melodus*) has a pale gray back and yellow legs and nests along the East Coast and by the waters of the center of the continent. The snowy plover (*Charadrius alexandrinus*) has pale gray upperparts, a break in the throat band, and dark legs. It is chiefly a western species but also has a Gulf of Mexico coastal population. The Wilson's plover (*Charadrius wilsonia*) has a dark back like the semipalmated plover, but the bill is longer and heavier, the breast band wider, and the feet dull pink. It nests locally on the Atlantic coasts.

Two other ring-necked plovers occur locally, in the far north. The ringed plover (*Charadrius hiaticula*) of Eurasia breeds in the high Arctic islands and the Mongolian plover (*Charadrius mongolus*) of Asia breeds in far western Alaska. Neither migrates through the United States.

KILLDEER AND MOUNTAIN PLOVER

In many northern states the killdeer (*Charadrius vociferus*) is one of the early arrivals and its plaintive "dee-ee kill-deee" is a welcome spring sound announcing the early disappearance of the remaining snow banks. The killdeer, 10 inches long, is really an oversize ring-neck plover with double breast band, a rufous rump, and a preference for open fields, pastures, and even large lawns as nesting and feeding habitats. But the actual nest site is likely to be on a bare spot, even in a parking lot or a railroad grade where the nest is a little hollow scraped by the bird with or without pebble added.

The injury-feigning display of the killdeer, used to distract an intruder from its nest, is one of the best-known and well-develloped distraction displays. It includes spreading and depressing its tail, holding up one wing and waving it as the bird drags itself along on the ground, uttering a distressed sounding "dee." The killdeer nests across the country and winters in the southern states where it sometimes goes in small flocks and frequents marshes and mudflats.

The mountain plover (*Eupoda montana*), 9 inches long, is a very plain bird in breeding dress, brownish above, with white forehead and underparts and a black line on the forecrown and from eye to bill. It nests on the northern short-grass prairies and winters in small flocks in open country to the south. Another plover, the dotterel (*Eudromias morinellus*) of Eurasia is casual in Alaska and may breed there.

BLACK-BELLIED AND GOLDEN PLOVERS

Both of these large plovers have the underparts black in breeding plumage and whitish in winter and in immature dress.

Although most of the black-bellied plovers (*Squatarola squatarola*), 12 inches long, winter on the coasts of Central and South America, a few are likely to be found sharing our southern beaches in winter with a few willets and parties of sanderlings. They are in white-bellied winter plumage

Killdeer (*Charadrius vociferus*)

but the whitish rump, the black tuft of feathers at the base of the underwing, and the plaintive whistled "pee-aa weep" make identification easy.
In April and May the spring migrants, now in breeding dress, are moving
through the northern states on the way to their tundra breeding grounds.
They complete their nesting cycle in a short time, for in July and
August many are on their way back south. The first arrivals in the northern states are still black-bellied but they soon start to moult and are followed by moulting adults and white-bellied young. The favorite feeding
places seem to be muddy flats and open, grassy fields.

The golden plover (*Pluvialis dominica*), 10 inches long, much like the
black-bellied plover but with a dark rump, gray tuft of feathers at the base
of the underwing, and more golden wash to its upperparts, also nests on the
tundra, but its migration is more remarkable. The birds nesting in the Canadian Arctic migrate south by flying southeast to the Atlantic coast and
then in flocks over water to South America where they winter in the grasslands of the southern part of the continent. On their return migration the
birds fly north through the interior of the United States, often stopping
to feed on the grassy plains. The birds of western Alaska, however, migrate
southwest over the sea to winter on the Pacific Islands and Australia.

SURFBIRD AND TURNSTONES

The surfbird and the turnstones look like stout, dark-colored sandpipers, 8-10 inches long, but their anatomy links them with the plovers. The surf from southern Alaska to the Straits of Magellan is the winter home of the surfbird (*Aphriza virgata*). At nesting time the birds fly to the high mountains of interior Alaska where they make their nests above timberline and switch to a diet of insects to replace the winter diet of marine invertebrates. The surfbird, 10 inches long, has much white in the tail and in summer is dark and streaked with gray. In winter it is mostly plain dark gray. The ruddy turstone (*Arenaria interpres*) gets its name from the reddish back in its breeding plumage and from its habit of turning over stones and seaweed as it rummages on the beaches for marine invertebrates. On its wintering grounds, however, it also eats berries, and punctures and eats tern's eggs. The complicated pattern of black and white shown in flight on wings, rump and tail is striking in both summer and winter plumage.

The related black turnstone (*Arenaria melanocephala*) nesting in Alaska and wintering on the Pacific coast is a darker bird with no rufous coloring.

Sandpipers *(Family Scolopacidae)*

The sandpipers that throng our beaches in August and September are probably the best known of several related families of shorebirds: the oyster-

catchers, the plovers, the sandpipers and the close relatives, the avocets and stilts, and the phalaropes. The sandpiper family is by far the most numerous in species and individuals and includes not only the many species of sandpipers but also the woodcock, snipe, dowitchers, godwits and curlews.

The nesting stronghold of the sandpiper family is the Arctic and Subarctic, in the barren grounds and the muskegs. Only a few nest south of the Canadian border. Breeding has a hurried tempo for the Arctic summer is short. Late summer sees the start of the autumn migration of shorebirds, most of them moving along our coastal flats and beaches and only a comparatively few traveling through the interior. Among these early migrants some still wear part of their breeding plumage, but soon all are in plainer winter plumage. Some birds winter in our southern states but some go as far as the Argentine. The spring migration is more hurried. Those species with colorful breeding plumage have already assumed it, and the migration through the interior and especially the Mississippi Valley is heavier. It is not unusual for a few non-breeding birds to summer far south of the breeding range.

The nest of sandpipers is typically a scantily lined hollow on the ground in which four heavily spotted eggs are laid. The finely patterned downy young are active from time of hatching, accompanying the parent and feeding themselves. The male often shares in family duties. The food is various, depending on what is available. On sea beach and mudflat small marine invertebrates predominate. Inland, insects are taken and a surprisingly wide variety of seeds, berries, small vertebrates and other items may be eaten. I once saw a sanderling eating a piece of buttered toast left from some picnic.

WOODCOCK AND SNIPE

Woodcock and snipe are unusual in the sandpiper family because they depend on their concealing coloration to avoid their enemies. Both birds are 10 to 12 inches long and have long bills and rather short legs.

Toward dusk in early spring a strange "peent" call from alder flat or birch-clad hill pasture tells the initiated that an American woodcock (*Philohela minor*) is present and is about to perform its aerial courtship. It is still light enough to see the bird circling upward with a whistling sound produced by its outer wing quills. At the top of its climb the bird levels off and with changes in its wing beats sends out bursts of wing-generated

Black turnstone (Arenaria melanocephala) 103

whistling notes. Finally the bird plunges earthward in a series of glides accompanied by vocal twitterings, and lands near its starting point, where it again gives its "peent." The performance may be repeated at intervals through the night and presumably serves a double purpose: to establish its territory and to attract or hold a female. In the northern part of its range the nest on the ground is made so early in the spring that late snowfalls may cover the incubating bird.

The woodcock usually sleeps away the day on a dry, brush-covered hillside where its mottled red-brown color harmonizes with the fallen leaves. At night it flies to a damp swale where it is easier to probe for the worms it likes, and in the morning the pencil-sized holes left by its probing and the white splashes of its droppings tell of its activities. It nests in the eastern half of the country and with the coming of frosts that harden the ground the northern wood-cocks move to the southeastern states.

The common snipe (*Capella gallinago*) is a bird of soggy meadows and bogs where it probes with its long bill for worms and depends on its buff and brown coloration to escape observation. Only when one is almost upon the hidden bird does it spring into the air and, uttering a harsh "scape's," darts away in a twisting zigzagging flight, which is one of the reasons sports men have prized it as a game bird.

In the spring, the snipe circles high above its breeding marsh or meadow and gives its peculiar winnowing or bleating flight song. The bleating is not vocal, but is caused by the rush of air past the tail quills as the bird changes course. The nest is hidden in the grass, and when an intruder approaches, the snipe may forsake its customary skulking ways and perch conspicuously on a branch and scold. The snipe nests across the northern part of the continent and winters in the southern part.

GODWITS

On the northern prairies where the ponds are also the nurseries of a great many ducks, I saw three large shorebirds on their nesting grounds: the willet, the long-billed curlew, and the marbled godwit (*Limosa fedora*). It was late June and the partly grown young godwits that had been hatched on the grassy plains were in the richer grass along the margin of the slough where insect food was more common. As I walked there it was usual for three or four of the noisy adults to be scolding overhead.

Most of these birds go to the California coast to winter on sandy beaches

Top: Willet (Catoptrophorus semipalmatus
Bottom: Lesser yellowlegs (Totanus flavipes

or on flats where they probe in the soft mud. Formerly the species had a wide prairie nesting range and many migrated to the eastern states.

Second in size only to the long-billed curlew, the marbled godwit is a buffy brown bird 16-20 inches long with an upturned bill from 3 to 5 inches long.

The Hudsonian godwit (*Limosa haemastica*) is a smaller bird, 14-17 inches long, that nests on the Arctic tundra and migrates to South America for the winter. It has a broad white bar across the base of the tail and its underparts are cinnamon in summer, whitish in winter. The related bar-tailed godwit (*Limosa lapponica*) with several bars on its tail nests in arctic Alaska and winters in the South Pacific Islands.

CURLEWS

The long, downcurved bills, large size, buffy brown plumage, and melodious whistled calls make the curlews a very distinct group. The long-billed curlew (*Numenius americanus*) standing on southern beaches in winter along with the smaller godwits and willets is impressive, but even more striking to me are the pairs of these great buffy brown birds with cinnamon wing linings flying low over the grasslands of the Great Plains. There they give their loud, wailing "cur-lee e e—," nest in the grass and eat insects. This curlew is the largest shorebird, old females reaching a length of 26 inches, including a 9-inch bill and a weight of two pounds. The related whimbrel (*Numenius phaeopus*), 17 inches long, is an arctic tundra nester and migrates along both coasts to winter in our southern states and southward. Its bill is only 3-4 inches long, and it has conspicuous dark streaks through the eye and along each side of the crown. The similar bristle-thighed curlew (*Numenius tahitiensis*) nests in Alaska and winters in the South Pacific Islands. The small Eskimo curlew (*Numenius borealis*), 13 inches long, that used to nest on the Arctic barrens and migrated in enormous numbers to winter in Argentina, is on the verge of extinction. There have been a few records of it in recent years, but individuals in the field are hard to distinguish from small whimbrels.

UPLAND PLOVER

The upland plover (*Bartramia longicauda*) nests and feeds in dense grass and that is why I have heard the mellow, rolling whistle of these birds in flight more often than I have seen them on the ground. The grasslands of

Top: *Marbled godwit* (*Limosa fedora*)   107
Bottom: *Long-billed curlew* (*Numenius americanus*)

the North Central states seem to be their main breeding areas now and they migrate through the eastern half of the country to winter in Argentina. The upland plover, 12 inches long, is a small curlew in structure with a straight sandpiper bill and a buffy brown plumage. It is called a plover from its habit of feeding on grassy fields as golden plovers did in the days of their former abundance.

WILLET

The willet (*Catoptrophorus semipalmatus*) is a large, gray shorebird about 15 inches long. With its flashing black and white wings and its loud call of "will-et" or "pill-will-willet," it is a very distinctive bird. I associate the bird with three very different habitats. In midsummer on the Alberta prairies when the young were running ahead of me along the edge of the sloughs, there were always several willets overhead, scolding. Along the roads in southwestern Nova Scotia where spruces fringed the salt marsh and meadow and willets nested in the grass, the willets seemed particularly incongruous perching and calling in the spruce tops. On the winter beaches of the Gulf of Mexico there are usually a few willets feeding along the water's edge. Most of them go farther south for the winter.

TATTLERS

The name tattler or telltale has its origin in the way the greater yellowlegs (*Totanus melanoleucus*) and some of its relatives spring up yelping and warn the whole marsh that a wildfowler is abroad. The greater yellowlegs, 14 inches long, nests in the bogs and muskegs of the Subarctic. In migration the flocks stop on mud flats and marshes. Here it is a wary, active, long-legged, slender bird with sharp, whistled calls and the habit of bobbing its head when about to fly. It winters from our southern states southward. The lesser yellowlegs (*Totanus flavipes*), 10 inches long, is a smaller, tamer, quieter version of the greater yellowlegs and also nests in the muskeg of the North.

The solitary sandpiper (*Tringa solitaria*), 8 inches long, is a smaller, darker, less noisy relative of the yellowlegs, going in small parties or solitary, and frequenting small bodies of water and marshes while in migration. It has a curious habit, upon alighting, of holding its wings extended over its back for a moment before folding them. It nests in trees in the North, laying its eggs in old bird's nests. The wandering tattler (*Heteroscelus*

Top: Spotted sandpiper (Actitis macularia)
Bottom: Dunlin (Erolia alpina)

incanum) nests in the interior of Alaska above timberline and winters chiefly on the Pacific islands.

SPOTTED SANDPIPER

The spotted sandpiper (*Actitis macularia*), 7½ inches long, is the only small sandpiper nesting across the central and northern United States. There it summers on gravelly and rocky shores of stream and river, pond and lake, near civilization or in wilderness areas. As one follows it along the shore, it flies out over the water with alternating short beats of its stiffly held wings and periods of gliding on downcurved wings while it gives sharp calls of "weet-wheet." The bird quickly lands again and wags its tail up and down in the exaggerated fashion that has given it the apt folk name of teeter-tail. The nest, with its four blotched eggs, is placed on the ground near the shore or in a field or even in cropland at some distance from the water and the downy young have the same tail-teetering habit as the adults. These sandpipers are said to dive and swim underwater to escape danger, and there is a record of one diving from the air to escape the strike of a pigeon hawk. The spotted sandpiper winters from our southern states southward and while a few may be loosely associated, this species, unlike most other sandpipers, does not flock and is not common on saltwater beaches or marshes. The spotted sandpiper is olive brown above and white below, and heavily spotted in summer.

SMALL SANDPIPERS

Each autumn beaches and mudflats swarm with small sandpipers that feed in flocks sometimes so large and dense as to look like a living carpet, each bird walking along, head down, industriously probing or pecking at the sand for tiny crustaceans or mollusks. When large flocks fly, the birds swirl and synchronize their turns so that from a distance the flocks look like drifting smoke. The semipalmated sandpiper in its thousands is usually the most common, but often one sees a number of species feeding together on the same stretch of beach. In all there are fifteen species of these small sandpipers, many of them so much alike as to puzzle the amateur, and the expert may have to look carefully to distinguish, for instance, a semipalmated from a western sandpiper.

All fifteen of these species nest on the barrens in the Arctic, the nursey of sandpipers. To avoid the beginning of the Arctic winter they migrate

110

southward early, begin to arrive on our beaches in late July, and are common there for weeks. Most go by way of the coasts but some go south through the interior, frequenting muddy ponds or shores. Some winter on our southern coasts, but most go on to southern South America. On their spring journey back north more of them travel through the interior of the United States and although they move more rapidly than on their southern migration they do rest and feed on muddy shores and flats.

Getting to know these birds requires a good illustrated guide book, seven-power binoculars, rubber boots and, if possible, the aid of an ornithologist. In the following, only an indication of the diversity of the fifteen species is attempted.

Some nine species of sandpipers are 6-9 inches long, have brownish streaked upperparts and are much alike in summer and winter plumage. The most common is the semipalmated sandpiper (*Ereunetes pusillus*), 6¼ inches long, of the sand flats. The western sandpiper (*Ereunetes mauri*), 6½ inches long, nests in Alaska. The rufous-necked sandpiper (*Erolia ruficolis*) of western Alaska is hardly separable from the semipalmated sandpiper in winter, though it has a rufous head in summer. The slightly smaller least sandpiper (*Erolia minutilla*), 6 inches long, is the only small sandpiper with yellow legs. The larger Baird's sandpiper (*Erolia bairdii*), 7 ½ inches long, has more of a scaled than streaked back pattern. The white-rumped sandpiper (*Erolia fuscicollis*), 7½ inches long, is distinguished by its white rump. The buff-breasted sandpiper (*Tryngites subruficollis*), 8 inches long, is a rather slender bird with a buffy breast; it favors dry, grassy interior habitats. Two larger sandpipers are the pectoral sandpiper (*Erolia melanotus*), 9 inches long, with a more heavily streaked breast and a preference for grassy places, and the related sharp-tailed sandpiper (*Erolia acuminata*), 9 inches long, a Eurasian species that nests in Alaska and migrates on our West Coast.

There are five other species of small sandpipers that have predominantly gray upperparts in winter plumage but in summer dress are different in appearance. The knot (*Calidris canutus*), 11 inches long, is the largest; in summer the breast is reddish, the back gray. The curlew sandpiper (*Erolia ferruginea*), 8 inches long, has its back brownish, its head and underparts red in summer. The dunlin (*Erolia alpina*), 8½ inches long, in summer has a reddish back and a black patch on the belly. The sanderling (*Crocethia alba*), 8 inches long, is very whitish in winter, reddish brown in sum-

mer. The stilt sandpiper (*Micropalama himantopus*), 8½ inches long, has very long legs. In summer the flanks are barred and there are rusty streaks on the head.

Two other species that frequent rocky coasts and winter only along American coasts are the purple sandpiper (*Erolia maritima*), 9 inches long, of the eastern Arctic and Atlantic coast, and the rock sandpiper (*Erolia ptilochemis*), 9 inches long, of Alaska and the West Coast.

DOWITCHERS

Despite their long, snipelike bills, the two dowitchers are large sandpipers that in migration fly and feed in close flocks. The dowitchers probe in mud-flats and shallow ponds and sometimes rest on beaches. Both species have large white patches on lower back and rump and have a gray winter plumage. The short-billed dowitcher (*Limnodromus griseus*), 11 inches long, and nesting in the Subarctic, has some reddish brown in summer dress, while the long-billed dowitcher (*Limnodromus scolopaceus*), 12 inches long, has underparts all red-brown and barred in summer. It nests in the Northwest and in migration is more common in the West.

Avocets and Stilts (*Family Recurvirostridae*)

Two tall, slender shorebirds with very long legs and distinctive bold color patterns, an avocet and a stilt, represent this family in the United States. The summer habitat of the American avocet (*Recurvirostra americana*) is shallow lakes, ponds and open water marshes of the plains and the arid basins of the West. A feeding avocet wades along swinging its long, slender upcurved bill back and forth through the water in front of it and seizing and swallowing any small organism it finds. Sometimes a flock of feeding birds line up abreast, shoulder to shoulder, and wade along as if driving their prey in front of them. When the mud under the water is soft, the webbing of their toes supports them. When the water is too deep for even their long legs, the birds swim.

The avocet pairs and makes a scant nest in a colony on the ground near water. If their four eggs are threatened by rising water the birds raise the eggs by adding to the nest, a height of 13 inches being recorded. The

Top: *Black-necked stilt* (*Himantopus mexicanus*)
Bottom: *American avocet* (*Recurvirostra americana*)

young are down-covered and not only run but swim at an early age. The avocet, 18 inches long, is white with black and white back and wings. In summer the head and neck are rust colored. The breeding range is western and the birds winter from our southern states to Central America.

The black-necked stilt (*Himantopus mexicanus*), 15 inches long, is remarkable for the length and slenderness of its legs, neck and bill. On land the bird has a graceful, deliberate walk, but its legs are so long it must bend them to pick food from the ground. However, it usually feeds by wading, daintily plucking insects from the water and from floating vegetation. The nest of this species is similar to that of the avocet and the stilt takes similar action against threatened flooding. The black-necked stilt, 15 inches long, is black above, white below, and breeds locally near shallow waters from Oregon to the Gulf of Mexico. It winters from southern states southward.

Phalaropes (*Family Phalaropodidae*)

Phalaropes, which may be described as sandpipers with webbed feet, can swim, and two of the three species even winter at sea, where they rest on the ocean in great flocks and feed on minute marine organisms picked from the surface. In migration they occur off American coasts. At nesting time they follow a sandpiper-like regime, except that the male takes over the family duties. The breeding plumage is bright and the female that takes the dominant role in courtship is the brightest. The winter and immature plumages are gray and white.

The red phalarope (*Phalaropus fulicarius*) is 8 inches long. In summer the female has the underparts deep red-brown, the back streaked and the face white. It nests in the high Arctic and winters at sea in the southern oceans. The northern phalarope (*Lobipes lobatus*) is 8 inches long and in summer the female has the underparts white with gray and red on the foreneck, and dark gray and brown upperparts. It nests in the Arctic and winters at sea in tropical and southern oceans.

The Wilson's phalarope (*Steganopus tricolor*) is 9 inches long and in summer the female has the underparts white, the upperparts mostly pale gray. It also has a black line from the eye down the side of the neck that becomes rufous red as it continues down the side of the back. In summer on prairie sloughs it walks about like a sandpiper, wades, and swims buoyantly. In feeding on the water this and the other phalaropes have the curious habit of spinning rapidly in one place, presumably setting up currents in the water that aid in catching small water animals. It secures these with quick jabs of its fine bill. In migration to its winter quarters in South American marshes it travels inland and along coastal marshes, sometimes associating with other shorebirds such as lesser yellowlegs.

Jaegers and Skua *(Family Stercorariidae)*

Although the gull-like jaegers and skua are quite able to walk and swim, as gulls do, they prefer to swoop down and seize their food while in flight, either as a predator or a pirate. On their breeding grounds on the northern tundra the jaegers (genus *Stercorarius*) feed on lemmings, eat the eggs and young of other birds, pursue and capture small birds on the wing and sometimes feed their small young on insects. Very different is their life the rest of the year; it is spent at sea. Moving southward in offshore waters of both coasts, the jaegers harry terns and gulls to make them drop or disgorge their prey, which the jaegers then catch in midair. When feeding tuna force schools of small fish to jump from the surface, jaegers swoop down, and at times these birds follow ships for galley scraps and fish offal. The wintering grounds of all three jaegers are at sea in southern oceans. The return migration in spring is evidently pelagic for few are seen in coastal waters at this time.

Courtship of jaegers on the tundra involves display flights. After mating, one to three eggs are laid in a scantily lined hollow and the downy young soon run about actively. Jaegers are bold and vociferous in protecting their nest and young. Sometimes they practice injury-feigning to lure away a potential enemy or may even dive at an intruding human and strike him on the head.

There are three species of jaegers and their general behavior and appearance are similar. Each has a dark color phase which is sooty black. The normal phase has gray upperparts with black cap and whitish underparts. In the adult plumage these species are best recognized by the shape and the amount of projection of the central tail feathers. The pomarine jaeger

(*Stercorarius pomarinus*) is 22 inches long, including the 5-inch projection of the blunt, twisted central tail feathers. The parasitic jaeger (*Stercorarius parasiticus*) is 18 inches long, including the 3-inch proejection of the pointed central tail feathers. The longtailed jaeger (*Stercorarius longicaudus*) is 21 inches long including the 5-8 inch projection of the pointed central tail feathers.

The skua (*Catharacta skua*) is 21 inches long, has a short tail and a dark brown plumage with a white patch in each wing. Its habits are in general those of the jaegers, but it is a heavier, more powerful and aggressive pirate and predator. Its distribution is remarkable: one population nests on sub-arctic Atlantic islands and winters at sea in the north Atlantic; others breed in the Antarctic and nearby islands and coasts; and some non-breeders visit the north Pacific, but almost always well off shore.

Gulls (*Family Laridae, part I*)

The long-winged, web-footed, gray and white gulls that patrol the sea beaches on foot, cruise and circle over inshore waters, float lightly offshore and gather screaming and yelping to feed on refuse from a fishing boat are as much a part of the coast to me as is the lapping of waves and the smell of the sea. Even the gulls that nest by inland lakes and on the prairies go to coast for the winter, and a few spend the winter at sea.

Little that can be eaten comes amiss to a hungry gull. It catches fish and eats any sea animal, dead or alive, that can be swallowed or torn to pieces. Ashore, in fields, it takes grasshoppers and worms, and in season, berries, and it even visits garbage dumps.

Somewhat gregarious at all times, gulls usually nest in small to very large colonies. The sexes are alike and both share family cares. An open nest is placed on the ground among reeds, on rocks or cliff ledges, often on islands off the coast or in lakes, and less often in trees. The three eggs are olive and brown-spotted, and the downy young run about soon after hatching but stay near the nest until they fly, the parents bringing food in their gullets from a distance. The color pattern of breeding adults is white with gray or black mantle, often with some black. Winter plumage may be duller and young birds of some gulls are grayer or browner and more black in var-

Top: *Herring gull* (*Larus argentatus*)
Bottom: *Immature herring gull*

ious patterns. The species are grouped in this way: gray mantled gull with black and white wing tips; white-winged gulls; black-backed gulls black-headed gulls and other gulls.

GRAY-MANTLED GULLS WITH BLACK AND WHITE WING TIP

If one sails from New York Harbor or San Francisco Bay in winter, the commonest gull in sight will be the herring gull (*Larus argentatus*) in various stages of plumage, perched on piers, scavenging about the wharfs and following departing steamers for a score of miles. The herring gull and some of its large relatives also have special feeding techniques. To open shellfish the gull flies up with a clam or a sea urchin in its bill and drops it onto rock or even a road, then follows it down and extracts the meat. Gull sometimes hover overhead where mergansers are fishing, and when a merganser comes to the surface with a fish in its bill, the gull seizes the prey and flies off with it. In spring the herring gulls move north to their nesting grounds on the northeast Atlantic coast, the interior lakes from the Great Lakes west to southern British Columbia, and north to the Arctic. This gull is 25 inches long and its breeding plumage is white with a gray mantle and black and white wing tips.

In 1848 the California gull (*Larus californicus*) earned a place in Utah history by eating the swarming crickets that were devouring the crops of the early Mormon settlers. One of the first laws passed in Utah was to protect this gull; it is the state bird and there is a monument to it in the Mormon Temple Grounds, Salt Lake City. The California gull is one of the conspicuous spring birds in northern Utah, arriving in late February and ranging widely over the countryside. It is omnivorous, relying heavily on grasshoppers and crickets, visiting streams for fishes, following the plow for whatever is turned up and visiting city parks and garbage dumps. In recent years the earlier reverence for the sea gull has lessened among sportsmen because of the birds' habit of eating wild duck eggs, and among cherry growers because the gulls try to share in the crop. These birds nest in dense colonies on rocky islands in Great Salt Lake where one census totaled 80,000 adults. Their neighbors include white pelicans, double-crested cormorants and great blue herons. By early autumn the birds leave for their wintering grounds. The California gull is similar to the herring gull but with greenish yellow, not pink legs, and it nests on interior lakes of the West It winters along the Pacific coast.

Laughing gull (Larus atricilla)

The ring-billed gull (*Larus delawarensis*), 19 inches long, is a smaller relative of the herring gull but with a black bar across its bill. It nests on interior lakes especially in the West, and winters commonly on both coasts. The mew gull (*Larus canus*), 17 inches long, is a still smaller relative of the herring gull that breeds in the Alaska–Mackenzie area as well as in Eurasia, sometimes building its nest in trees. It winters along the Pacific coast.

WHITE-WINGED GULLS

There are three large white gulls with gray mantles and white wings tips. The glaucous-winged gull (*Larus glaucescens*), 26 inches long, is the common nesting gull of the Pacific coast islands from Alaska to Washington and it winters south to California. The larger glaucous gull (*Larus hyperboreus*), about 30 inches long, is an Arctic breeder coming south in winter along the coast in the east to New York and in the west to California where it frequents the outer shoreline. The related but considerably smaller Iceland gull (*Larus glaucoides*), 24 inches long, is also an Arctic nester. It comes south in winter along the Atlantic coast to New England.

BLACK-BACKED GULLS

Two gulls are characterized by being white with a black mantle in adult plumage. The great black-backed gull (*Larus marinus*), 30 inches long, is one of the very large gulls, and is a scavenger as well as a predator, eating other sea birds, their eggs and young. It is a north Atlantic species, nesting south to New York and in winter south to Carolina and inland to the Great Lakes. The similar but smaller western gull (*Larus occidentalis*), is a west coast, saltwater bird, nesting on rocky islands from Washington to California. It has been called an inveterate egg-eater of the sea bird colonies; at other seasons it shares in the bounty of the seashore with other gulls.

BLACK-HEADED GULLS

The black head of the six species of gulls grouped here is a conspicuous mark in summer, but is reduced to a few patches in winter. The wing patterns remain the same. The light, buoyant flight and the general quickness and agility of the laughing gull (*Larus atricilla*) contrasts with the steadier flight and gait of the larger gulls. The laughing gull does eat dead fish and other jetsam, shares with the ring-billed gull a readiness to snap up scraps tossed them by picnickers on Florida beaches, and pilfers fish from brown pelicans. But, in general, the laughing gull prefers live rather than dead food. It hovers over the water and picks fish from the surface, catches insects on the wing, and walks nimbly over mudflats chasing crabs and eating other marine invertebrates. The laughing gull, 17 inches long, has a solid black wing tip. It nests locally in large colonies on sandy islands of the Atlantic and Gulf of Mexico coasts, and is the only gull breeding in the southeastern states.

The related but slightly smaller Franklin's gull (*Larus pipixcan*), with subterminal white spots in its dark wing tips, nests in large colonies in the reed beds of prairie lakes and migrates to the Gulf of Mexico and to South America for the winter. The Bonaparte's gull (*Larus philadelphia*), 13 inches long, has a large, triangular white area in the outer part of the wing. It nests in spruce trees near water in the far Northwest and winters on both coasts. The Sabine's gull (*Xema sabini*), 14 inches long, has a black and white triangular pattern in its wings, a forked tail, arctic nesting grounds, and winters off the Pacific coast to Peru. The black-headed gull (*Larus rudibundus*), 13 inches long, is a European species that straggles to the

Atlantic coast. It is similar to Bonaparte's gull but with a red instead of a black bill. The little gull (*Larus minutus*), 11 inches long, was considered a straggler from the Old World until 1962 when several nests were found in a marsh in southern Ontario. Its upper wing surface is all gray.

OTHER GULLS

The Heerman's gull (*Larus heermanni*) nests on islands off western Mexico and in autumn visits the Pacific coast north to Vancouver Island where it is a bird of the coastline. It has a peculiar pattern for a gull: head white, otherwise gray with a darker gray mantle and black wing and tail quills. The Ross's gull (*Rhodostethia rosea*), an Arctic bird, a casual visitor south to the Bering Sea in winter, is small, 13 inches long, gray and white tinged rosy, and is the only gull with a pointed tail. The ivory gull (*Pagophila eburnea*), 16 inches long, is rarely seen south of the Arctic and is the only gull with pure white plumage and black legs. The kittiwakes, 17 inches long, are white gulls with gray mantles and solid black wing tips. They nest on little ledges on cliffs in the north. The red-legged kittiwake (*Rissa brevirostris*) is a Bering Sea species and the black-legged kittiwake (*Rissa tridactyla*) nests from Alaska to Labrador. Although it winters off both coasts it usually stays at sea and is the only pelagic gull.

Terns (*Family Laridae, part II*)

Over coastal waters the long-winged gray and white terns beat back and forth watching for fish, which they catch by diving head first from the air. Successful or not, they fly up at once, for despite their webbed feet they rarely sit on the water or swim. To rest they perch on the beach near the water's edge, on sandbars or on floating driftwood, and being more sociable than gulls, usually gather in flocks. Their nests are usually in colonies of a few pair to thousands of birds; offshore, sandy islands are favorite places for them. The nests are usually on the ground and are scrapes or hollows with little or much lining. Three olive or buff-brown spotted eggs are common and the downy young stay at or near the nest for a time, after which they may run about or even swim, but they are fed near the nest until they can fly. Some nest by inland waters and a few in marshes. An intruder in a tern's colony is scolded vociferously by a cloud of birds overhead.

Common tern (Sterna hirundo

Terns are a tropical group. Only one species is an Arctic nester, and all migrate south in winter though some individuals winter on our southern waters. In all, we have fourteen species of regular occurrence. Most of them are remarkably uniform in shape and color, but vary in size from 9 inches to 21 inches in length.

COMMON TERN AND NEAR RELATIVES

When small fishes jump out of the water to escape predatory mackerels, the hungry common terns (*Sterna hirundo*) that have been beating back and forth across the bay converge on the spot. A tern partly closes its wings, goes head first into the water, pops back to the surface, takes wing, shakes itself free of water, swallows the fish and goes after another. Other terns see this and soon there is a whole swarm of shrieking, plunging terns. Suddenly the school of fish go down beyond reach of the terns and the birds drift away. Some continue to forage, some line up, head to the wind, on the beach, and some may go to relieve their incubating mates. The colonies of a few to hundreds of nests are on coastal islands; the nests are on open sandy or gravelly beaches, near sparse, low vegetation. The breeding range is from Alberta to Labrador, south to the Great Lakes region and along the coast to North Carolina, also locally on the Gulf of Mexico coast. The main wintering areas are on South American coasts.

The common tern, 15 inches long, with a long, deeply forked tail and a red, black-tipped bill, has the basic tern pattern: white with black cap and gray mantle. Three other species are very similar in appearance but have different ranges. The Forster's tern (*Sterna forsteri*) breeds chiefly in the marshes of inland waters from California and Alberta to the Great Lakes region and also locally on islands off the southeastern states; it winters to South America. The arctic tern (*Sterna paradisaea*) with an all red bill is an abundant Arctic breeder. Most individuals migrate over water and some go as far as the Antarctic. The roseate tern (*Sterna dougallii*) with a black bill breeds along the central Atlantic coast and winters from the West Indies southward.

CRESTED TERNS

Three species of crested terns are much like the common tern in color, but are larger and have a paler mantle, shorter, less deeply forked tail and a short black crest. The largest is the royal tern (*Thalasseus maximus*), 20

inches long, with a red bill. It nests in great colonies on the flat, sandy coastal islands from Maryland to Texas (California records are of non-breeders from Mexico). The related sandwich tern (*Thalasseus sandvicensis*) is somewhat smaller, 16 inches long, has a black bill, and nests on the sandy coastal islands of the southeastern states, often in colonies with royal terns. The elegant tern (*Thalasseus elegans*), 19 inches long, is similar to the royal tern but smaller and wanders to the California coast after nesting on the west Mexico coast.

CASPIAN TERN

As large as a medium-sized gull, the Caspian tern (*Hydroprogne caspia*) is our largest tern and its appearance and behavior is in general like the smaller terns of the ocean beaches. But it lacks the grace of the smaller terns and appears to be a stouter, stronger bird. The large, red bill, large head and short, slightly forked tail contribute to this impression. Besides plunging for fish it has some gull or even jaeger habits. It sometimes alights on the water to feed like a gull and is said to take and eat the eggs and young of other birds. Less sociable than many terns, it is often seen alone and its colonies are small, though these may sometimes be associated with large colonies of other terns and gulls. The Caspian tern, 21 inches long, nests on lakes and coastal islands in the temperate and subarctic latitudes.

LEAST TERN

The least tern (*Sterna albifrons*) is our smallest tern. In keeping with its small size it is a dainty bird with a light graceful flight over the water. It hovers for a moment to locate a fish, then plunges down to seize it, or flying lower, snatches a fish from the surface. The least tern prefers to nest in a series of small colonies on sandy beaches such a piping plovers use, where the eggs and young match the beach so closely as to be almost invisible. The least tern, 9 inches long, has a white forehead and yellow bill. It nests not only along the Atlantic and California coasts but on sandbars in the Mississippi River and it winters to South America.

GULL-BILLED TERN

Once very abundant, the gull-billed tern (*Gelochelidon nilotica*) now has a scattered summer distribution in southern California and on the coasts of southeastern states where it feeds commonly over the salt marshes as well as on the edge of the sea. Unlike other terns, it sometimes feeds on foot and eats a wide variety of animal life. About 15 inches long, the mantle is very pale, almost white, and the heavy bill is black.

BLACK TERN

Unlike other terns, the black tern (*Chlidonias niger*) is black in summer with a gray mantle and tail. It is a bird of the summer marshes of the interior of the continent from the Great Lakes to Oregon. In feeding, its rather broad wings move through a shallow arc as the bird patrols a few feet or yards above the weed-filled water, giving sharp little cries and every now and then daintily dropping down and, without alighting, plucking an insect from the surface. On the prairie sloughs of Alberta where it also feeds over marsh vegetation and richer grasslands much as it does over water, I found it a rather tame, almost friendly bird. As I drove through the prairies, I saw the birds gather to snap up insects frightened into activity by the slowly moving car. At times when insects are plentiful it hawks for them in the air and then it vaguely resembles a feeding nighthawk.

Its rudimentary nest is on a mat of floating reed stems or on an old muskrat house, often in loose colonies. In the autumn the black tern, which is 9 inches long with a nearly square tail, has the black of head, neck and body mostly replaced by white. It then goes to the sea coasts to feed.

TERNS OF THE DRY TORTUGAS

Three terns of tropical waters reach the United States territory regularly only on the Dry Tortugas, islets west of the Florida Keys. The sooty tern (*Sterna fuscata*) with black upperparts and white underparts nests on the Tortugas in great numbers. The noddy tern (*Anous stolidus*), brown and blackish except for a white cap, also nests there and is unusual among terns in building a nest in trees or bushes. The related but smaller and blacker black noddy tern (*Anous tenuirostris*) is a regular visitor there.

Skimmers (*Family Rynchopidae*)

The ternlike skimmer flies over calm, inshore waters, fishing with the lower mandible of its widely opened bill cutting the surface. When the lower mandible makes contact with a small fish the bill snaps shut, the head jerks down and back, and the catch is made; it is eaten in flight and the skimmer continues its fishing. The adaptation for this is in the bill, the lower mandible being much longer than the upper one and compressed to knife-blade thinness.

Along the Atlantic coast, from New Jersey to the Gulf of Mexico, the black skimmer (*Rynchops nigra*) nests and rests on sand beaches and feeds over adjacent waters. It is gregarious in feeding and when resting. Standing on a sandbar the birds line up, closely spaced, head to wind. Their blackness, the upward-slanting, folded wing tips and large, downward-pointing bill and short legs give them a very distinctive appearance.

Gregarious also when nesting, the colonies are on sandy beaches above high tides, the four eggs being laid in little hollows in the sand. If the nest is robbed, a second is made and new clutch of eggs laid. The downy young are fed near the nest until they fly. The black skimmer, 18 inches long, is black above, white below, with long broad wings and a conspicuous black and red bill.

The Auk Family *(Family Alcidae)*

The auks and their near relatives with such strange sounding names as murre, razorbill, guillemot, puffin, dovekie, auklet and murrelet are distantly related to the gulls but are adapted to a quite different way of life. The auks have short legs, webbed feet and short wings and are swimming and diving birds. They spend their winters at sea, resting on the water and diving to seek their food of fish and small marine invertebrates underwater. These birds come to land only to nest, usually in large colonies on islands or sea-facing cliffs. The one or two eggs are laid on a rock ledge, in a rock crevice or in a tunnel dug by the birds. The downy young in some species are raised in the nest, in others they follow the parent to sea at an early age. The group is a northern one nesting chiefly in the Arctic and Subarctic and wintering in temperate zone waters. The Bering Sea is especially rich in species. There are twenty species, ranging from 6 to 18 inches in length. Black and white plumage in simple patterns is a common type of coloration. A few species have grotesquely enlarged bills and others bizarre head plumes

MURRES

Thousands of the white-breasted common murre (*Uria aalge*) line and crowd the wide ledges and tops of sea cliffs at nesting time from California to the Bering Sea on the Pacific and in the Gulf of St. Lawrence area of the Atlantic coast. These conspicuous birds are the unoccupied ones awaiting their turn to incubate. The incubating birds are farther back on the ledges with their black backs turned to the sea and each is half crouched over its single egg on the bare rock. When the birds are alarmed by a human intruder they seem to pour off the ledges, so great is their number. Some eggs fall from the ledges and are lost but the near conical shape of the egg seems an adaptation for it to roll in a small circle, rather then off the edge. With rapid wing beats and direct flight, the murres often fly as far as twelve miles to favorite fishing places, where they splash down, swim and dive to catch their prey underwater. The food is brought to the single downy young on the ledges until the young one is partly grown and can jump and tumble into the sea and swim away.

The thick-billed murre (*Uria lomvia*) is a more northern counterpart of the common murre and nests on smaller ledges in lesser concentrations, but the ranges of the two overlap broadly. The murres, 17 to 18 inches long, have pointed bills, blackish upperparts and white underparts, and in summer they have black throats. The two species differ only in detail such as in the more slender bill of the common murre.

MURRELETS

Some 20,000 pairs of ancient murrelets (*Synthliboramphus antiquum*) have been estimated to breed on Forrester Island, southeastern Alaska, in May and June. In their colonies the earth is riddled with burrows where the two eggs are laid. Not a bird is to be seen about the island in the daytime, one parent incubating underground, the off duty bird away at sea, feeding and loafing. The colony comes to life in the brief Arctic night when there is a continual coming and going of birds. When the two eggs have hatched and the downy young in the burrows are about four days old, the parents, chirping encouragement, lead the noisy young tumbling and scrambling down to the sea. The adults dive through the waves and the young follow. By morning they are out of sight of the island, not to return until the next breeding season. The winter is spent at sea or in offshore coastal waters as far south as California, often in groups of various sizes.

The ancient murrelet, 10 inches long, has dark gray upperparts with a black head, white underparts, and in summer has a black throat and a white line above the eye. It nests from the Aleutian Islands to Queen Charlotte Islands. The related marbled murrelet (*Brachyramphus marmoratum*) is common in summer in the intracoastal waterways from south Alaska to Washington and probably nests on or in the ground in the coniferous forests inland, while the Kittlitz's murrelet (*Brachyramphus brevirostre*) is its paler northern counterpart. In southern California are two other species, the Xanthus murrelet (*Endomychura hypoleuca*) nesting on the Santa Barbara Islands and the Craveri's murrelet (*Endomychura craveri*) which breeds farther south and wanders north to California.

AUKLETS

Many naturalists travelling in the Bering Sea have written of the abundance of the least auklet (*Aethia pusilla*), of these 6-inch birds swarming like mosquitoes, or appearing in the distance like smoke about their island homes. When Dr. A. M. Bailey was walrus hunting for the Denver Museum at the Diomedes Islands he found these birds already abundant in early June even though winter conditions prevailed, ice floes crowded against the islands and all but the steepest slopes were still snow covered. In the early morning great lines of the birds flew from the islands out over the Bering Straits. Later, as the hunter's oomiak pushed through the floes, pairs of least auklets were continually flushing, with little cries, from the narrow water lanes, and on large openings there were rafts of thousands of the twittering birds on the water. Presumably they slept in rock crevices in the snow-free cliffs. Eggs were not recorded until July. Southward movements began in September. The least auklet, 6 inches long, is mostly black above, white below, with brownish flanks and a red bill in summer. It breeds on islands in the whole Bering Sea area and winters at sea south to the Aleutians and off Japan.

There are five other auklets, ranging in size from 7 to 13 inches long. Three of these breed only in the Bering Sea—Aleutian Island area: the crested auklet (*Aethia cristatella*) with a curly crest and white face plumes; the whiskered auklet (*Aethia pygmaea*) with a curly crest and two sets of face plumes; and the parakeet auklet (*Cyclorrhynchus psittacula*) with a single set of face plumes. A fourth species breeding from southeastern Alaskan islands to the State of Washington is the rhinoceros auklet (*Ceror-*

hinca monocerata), the largest species, with a horny projection at the base of the bill and two sets of face plumes. The fifth species, breeding from southeastern Alaska to islands off California, is the Cassin's auklet (*Ptychoramphus aleutica*), a small plain species.

PUFFINS, AUKS, GUILLEMOTS AND DOVEKIE

The great, compressed, red and black bill of the common puffin (*Fratercula arctica*) makes it unmistakable and, with its odd antics as it walks about nimbly on its red feet, it gives the appearance of being a droll, bumbling fellow in fancy dress. It is the only Atlantic member of the auk family to dig a burrow for a nest, and its breeding range is from Maine northward. On the Pacific coast lives the related horned puffin (*Fratercula corniculata*) and also the tufted puffin (*Lunda cirrhata*), which is black with a white face and yellow ear tufts.

Like the murres in size and color the razorbill (*Alca torda*) of the northern Atlantic coast has a bill that is neither tapered nor pointed but is compressed and blunt tipped. The razorbill nests in rock crevices, often hidden from sight, and its colonies are small. The razorbill is the nearest living relative of the extinct great auk (*Pinguinus impennis*).

The guillemots in summer plumage are black auks, 13 inches long, with big white wing patches and red feet. The black guillemot (*Cepphus grylle*) of the East nests in rock crevices from Maine northward. The pigeon guillemot (*Cepphus columba*) of the Pacific nests from California northward.

The dovekie (*Plautus alle*) is the only tiny auk of the Atlantic. It nests in Greenland in enormous numbers in the crevices of rock fields and talus slopes and flies about in large flocks that recall swarms of insects. It winters in southern Greenland waters in openings in the ice floes and southward in arctic currents south to off North Carolina. In some years severe storms force the birds southward and at such times many birds come ashore and perish from Maine to Florida. The dovekie, 8 inches long, is black above, white below, with a black throat and breast in summer.

Pigeons and Doves (*Family Columbidae*)

The cooing notes of pigeons and doves are their best-known characteristics

Common puffin (Fratercula arctica

and the introduced pigeon of city streets is the best-known species. Although sixteen species have been recorded in the United States, less than half of them are common and widespread enough to be an appreciable part of our avifauna. These are birds that range from 7 to 16 inches long, walk on the ground, perch in trees, eat seeds and fruit and have subdued coloration. Pairs are formed and both males and females share in domestic duties. Frail nests of twigs are built and usually two white eggs are laid. The young are cared for in the nest until they can fly.

MOURNING DOVE

In some states the mourning dove (*Zenaidura macroura*) is a game bird; in others, it is a song bird. Certainly it seems a song bird to me, for its mournful sounding "coo coo coo" is part of the spring chorus to which robin, cardinal and tufted titmouse also contribute. Soon a pair is trying out branches in maple, apple and spruce trees about the yard for a nest site, and then walking about the garden picking up twigs for the frail platform on which two white eggs are laid. An exasperating thing about the mourning doves that nest in our garden is that sooner or later the incubating bird is likely to be startled from its nest and knock out one or both eggs. No wonder nesting continues through spring and summer. Some late nests may follow an early successful one, but others may be second or third tries at nesting.

After nesting, the mourning dove gathers into loose flocks, feeds on seeds and grain in fields, visits roadsides for gravel, flies to favorite drinking places and roosting trees. It nests across the United States and is migratory only in the North. It is a short legged, plump breasted bird about 12 inches long with a long, pointed tail and brown and buffy plumage.

WHITE-WINGED DOVE

In Arizona the white-winged dove (*Zenaida asiatica*) used to cause so much damage to the grain crop that sorghum growers now plant late so their crop ripens after the birds have left for their winter headquarters in Mexico. The white-wing is similar to a mourning dove but with a rounded tail and white patches in wings and tail. In summer the birds favor river bottom lands and flats of the Southwest where there are mesquite thickets, willow and cotton-woods with adjacent fields, croplands and desert. The white-

Top: *Tufted puffins* (*Lunda cirrhata*)
Bottom: *Pigeon guillemots* (*Cepphus columba*)

wing feeds on seeds and grain in the open and on the fruits and flowers of cactus and trees where it perches. When the birds are plentiful the nests are in large colonies which the cooing of the males make conspicuous. Nesting over, the doves gather into flocks and on their swift, straight flights to watering places give sportsmen prized wing shooting.

The white-winged dove breeds in Mexico and the Southwest, from the Rio Grande Valley to southeastern California. Some return to Mexico for the winter.

BAND-TAILED PIGEON

The band-tailed pigeon (*Columba fasciata*) often perches high in the oak and coniferous trees of the western mountains. It is one of our largest pigeons, 15 inches long, recalling the pigeon of city streets, but it is larger, darker and has a pale band on the end of its tail and a white half collar on its hind neck. Outside the breeding season the band-tail goes in flocks and feeds on acorns, seeds and flowers among the branches of trees and on berries in shrubs, and visits cultivated fields for grain. Flocks wander widely to find food and great numbers sometimes congregate in favorite places. At nesting time the pairs scatter. Some of the cooing of the males is so deep that it might be mistaken for the hooting of an owl. The flat nest is sometimes well up in a tree and but a single egg is laid. The range of the species is from British Columbia to Central America. Northern birds move southward in winter with notable concentrations in southern California.

GROUND DOVE

The tiny, short-tailed ground dove (*Columbigallina passerina*) is a common, familiar bird of our southern states. In our Florida dooryard a pair walks daily with quick, short steps and nodding head, picking up grass and weed seeds and grains of sand. When startled the birds sometimes fly but a little way, with jerking flight and a flash of rufous in the wings, or they go farther with swift direct flight. In the long breeding season, from February to October, the male often perches on our telephone wire and calls "coo-oo" over and over. The nest, with its two eggs, is placed on the ground or low in a shrub or tree. The ground dove, 7 inches long, is generally dull brownish and ranges from South Carolina to southeastern California, favoring open sandy places where water is available.

Mourning dove (Zenaidura macroura)

OTHER PIGEONS AND DOVES

The small, long-tailed Inca dove (*Scardafella inca*) occurs locally in the Southwest in fields and roadsides and seems to favor the vicinity of human habitations, even frequenting city parks. This dove is 8 inches long, its grayish plumage has a scaled pattern, and the range is from southeast Texas to southern Arizona.

There are four pigeons and doves of the West Indies that occur or have been recorded on the Florida Keys. The white-crowned pigeon (*Columba leucocephala*), 13 inches long, is a dark pigeon with a white crown that comes each year to nest in the mangroves. The zenaida dove (*Zenaida aurita*), the Key West quail-dove (*Geotrygon chrysia*) and the ruddy quail dove (*Geotrygon montana*) are of rare or accidental occurrence on the Keys. The wooded country of the lower Rio Grande Valley is the farthest north reached by the red-billed pigeon (*Columba flavirostris*) and the white-fronted dove (*Leptotila verreauxi*), both of Mexico and Central America.

Three species of doves and pigeons have been introduced into the United States and have become established. The rock dove (*Columba livia*) of Eurasia is the ancestor of the common domestic pigeon that is so well known on city streets and parks as well as in half-wild flocks about farms and as a completely wild bird where grain and shelter are available. The ancestral plumage is shown by the common, 13-inch-long, blue-gray birds, but many fancy varieties have been developed, and white and mottled individuals are seen in wild flocks. The spotted dove (*Streptopelia chinensis*), a brownish bird, 13 inches long and with a speckled black and white collar on its hind neck, is a Chinese species that has become established in parts of southwestern California. The ringed turtledove (*Streptopelia risoria*), 12 inches long, is a very pale bird with a black bar on its hind neck. It has long been a cage bird in the Old World and its precise origin is unknown. Introduced into America, it is established about the cities of Los Angeles, Tampa and Miami.

The extinct passenger pigeon (*Ectopistes migratorious*), a 16-inch-long bird with a tail long and pointed and plumage bluish slate, olive-brown and vinaceous, was enormously abundant in colonial times in the eastern part of the continent, but the impact of civilization wiped out the species by the early part of the present century. The last living specimen died at the Cincinnati Zoological Garden in 1914.

Parrots (*Family Psittacidae*)

The parrots are a tropical group and at present no species occur naturally in the United States. One Mexican species has visited the southwestern states and our only native species has been exterminated.

The home of the thick-billed parrot (*Rhynchopsitta pachyrhyncha*) is in Mexico but at long and irregular intervals great flocks have invaded the pine forests of the mountains of southern New Mexico and Arizona. The latest major invasions were in 1904 and 1917-18. The birds gathered into roosts of as many as a thousand birds to sleep in the pines. During the day they broke up into smaller parties and flew with swift direct flight and screeching calls to seek out pine cones, ripe or green, from which they tore the seeds, their main food. This parrot, 16 inches long with a short, pointed tail, is green with red in the forepart of head and in wings.

Early travellers wrote of the great flocks of the now extinct Carolina parakeet (*Conuropsis carolinensis*) in the eastern half of the United States. In the early part of the present century the last of the birds disappeared,

Roadrunner (Geococcyx californianus)

victims of civilization. About 13 inches long, with a long pointed tail, this parakeet was green with orange and yellow head.

Several exotic parrots, escaped from captivity, are sometimes found at large, even far from towns.

Cuckoos, Anis and Roadrunners

(Family Cuculidae)

The tree-living cuckoos, the brush and grassland anis and the ground-living roadrunners make a strange assemblage of cuckoos. The evidence is of course anatomical, best seen externally in the arrangement of the toes—two in front, two behind. Unlike some cuckoos, all the American species make their own nests and tend their own young.

TREE CUCKOOS

Living among the leafy shelter of forest shade trees and hedgerows, the three tree cuckoos, 12 inches long, are slender birds of elegant appearance with very small feet and long tails and an appetite for hairy caterpillars. The nest, in a tree or shrub, is a shallow basin of twigs; two to four blue-green eggs are laid in it.

You are more likely to hear than to see the yellow-billed cuckoo (*Coccyzus americanus*); its song is a series of wooden "kuks" followed by a series of "cows" given as the bird sits motionless amongst the leaves. Caterpillars are its favorite food, which it gathers with slow, deliberate movements. Alarmed, it slips away and disappears. In flight, with its slashing wing-beats and long tail, this cuckoo may recall the much plumper mourning dove. The range of the yellowbill is across the continent and its winter quarters are in South America. The large white spots on the tips of the outer tail feathers, the rufous area on the wing quills, and the yellow in the bill are the distinguishing marks of this bird; otherwise it is olive-brown above and white below.

The related black-billed cuckoo (*Coccyzus erythropthalmus*) is similar; I have seen both species feeding on abundant caterpillars that were denuding catalpa trees of their leaves. The ranges of the two species overlap but the blackbill is a more northern and woodland species that extends only

138

as far west as the prairies. Its distinguishing characters are the small tail spots, lack of rufous in the wings and the all-black bill. The mangroves cuckoo (*Coccyzus minor*) of the tropics extends north only to the mangroves of southern Florida and its coloration consists of buffy underparts and a black face patch.

ANIS

At first glance, a flock of anis perched in a clump of reeds might be mistaken for grackles, despite their high, compressed bills. Their weak flight, however, is distinctive, consisting of a few wing flaps and then a long glide. These birds, usually in flocks, walk over the grass catching insects, including those stirred up by cattle. In nesting, the anis build a communal nest in which several pairs lay their eggs. Anis are tropical, and the groove-billed ani (*Crotophaga sulcirostris*), 12 inches long, occurs in our area only in grass and brushlands of the Lower Rio Grande Valley. The related smooth-billed ani (*Crotophaga ani*), 13 inches ling, has colonized in south Florida.

ROADRUNNER

The fleet-footed roadrunner (*Geococcyx californianus*) of the Southwest has been clocked at the amazing speed of 15 miles per hour, which is the grain of truth in the fiction that a roadrunner can outrun a horse. The roadrunner eats small snakes, up to a foot long, and this has been elaborated into the folktale that it battles and kills rattlesnakes. But the roadrunner needs no embellishment to make it a character. It is a most unusual bird. Two feet long and looking like a scrawny brown chicken with a very long tail, it runs with long strides, head down and tail streaming, flicking a wing to help in a turn and leaving X-shaped tracks in the dust. Pausing, it raises its head and slowly cocks up its tail. Its flapping and sailing flight is decidedly a secondary mode of locomotion.

Lizards, small snakes and mice, the roadrunner's food, are pursued, caught and beaten into quiescence; small birds are stalked and snatched from their flight, and insects, large and small, are picked from ground, air or from bushes into which the roadrunner climbs. The nest is placed in shrub or cactus and in it the bird lays a half-dozen or so whitish eggs at long intervals so that eggs and young in various stages of development may be found in the same nest.

The roadrunner's favorite habitat combines brush or cactus thickets and open ground. While the roadrunner has lost some of its territory in California through the encroachment of civilization, it has also gained some by spreading eastward into clearings in the oak-covered Ozark Mountains.

Barn Owls (*Family Tytonidae*)

The white, heart-shaped face, the nearly white underparts, and the habit of sleeping in disused buildings make the barn owl (*Tyto alba*) a very distinctive bird. However, it usually escapes being seen by sleeping away the day in dark places, not only in lofts, barns and steeples but also in holes in trees, caves in cliffs and in wells and mine shafts. By night the barn owl flies over open country searching for small animals which it can locate by ear and seize in complete darkness. Rats and mouse-sized mammals are a favorite prey and it takes many house rats when it lives in towns and on the edges of cities. I even saw a barn owl perched under a cornice of the Field Museum, Chicago, and they have been recorded as nesting in a tower of the Smithsonian Institution building in Washington. No nest material is brought, the five to eleven white eggs being laid on the floor, where debris from pellet and prey accumulates. It is 18 inches long, a slender bird with a large head, dark eyes, rather long, nearly bare legs, white or buffy white below and gray and buffy above. In America it ranges across the continent from southern Canada to South America.

Owls (*Family Strigidae*)

Most owls, clad in browns and grays, are birds of the night, with hooked claws and beaks for seizing and tearing animal prey. The owl's large eyes are set in feathered disks and look straight ahead. The feather head tufts of some owls, referred to as "ears" or "horns" in their names, have nothing to do with hearing or horns. Pairs are formed, the white eggs are laid in an old bird's nest, a hole in a tree, a nest on the ground or in a burrow.

Top: Great horned owl (Bubo virginianus)
Bottom: Spotted owl (Strix occidentalis)

and the young are cared for by both parents. There are seventeen species of owls and one species of barn owl in America, ranging from 6 to 29 inches long in size.

SCREECH OWLS

The screech owl (*Otus asio*) commonly nests in holes in the shade trees of the little town in which I live outside of Chicago and each year they sing in the spring. But on January 24th and 25th, 1967, a screech owl sang all evening from the maple tree on the corner, an unprecedented winter event. Then on January 26th came the blizzard that immobilized all wheeled traffic in Chicago for days. Such is the stuff of which superstitions are made, just as the call of a "shivering owl" from above a Cajun cabin roof is supposed to foretell disaster and death.

The song of the screech owl is a tremulous whistle, almost a hollow rolling trill, used at mating time when the birds pair. A hollow in a tree or an old woodpecker hole is used for a nest. By early summer the young can fly but are still fed for a time on a wide variety of small animals, among which large insects and mice are most common. The screech owl, 10 inches long, has a pair of short ear tufts, a short tail, yellow eyes and a mottled pattern of whitish and red-brown or gray-brown, depending on the color phase, with some black streaks and cross-barring on the whitish underparts. Depending on its mood, a screech owl may appear short and plump, or long and slender. It ranges over much of the United States in hardwood stands, woodlots and shade trees.

The related whiskered owl (*Otus trichopsis*), 9 inches long, of Central America ranges north to southern Arizona, and the similar flammulated owl (*Otus flammeolus*), 7 inches long, differing in the dark eyes, shorter ear tufts and in favoring coniferous forets, is a bird of the western mountain region.

GREAT HORNED OWL

The great horned owl (*Bubo virginianus*) is the big hoot owl or cat owl of all the wooded parts of the continent. It has survived chiefly in wilderness or in remote areas, for it is a formidable predator. With an implacable glare of yellow eyes, and "horns" that give it a cat-like look, it has a reputation for savagery that is greatly exaggerated. Actually, in the wild it depends on mammals up to the size of rabbits and birds up to that of grouse

Young great horned owl (Bubo virginianus)

and duck. It is a magnificent raptorial bird without which the wilderness would be poorer. Now, with more tolerance for the roles of predator and prey in the balanced ecology of our country, the horned owl is less persecuted and nests nearer settlement. In Amherst, Nova Scotia, a nest was built in a shade tree over a main thoroughfare of the town and, under police protection, the brood was peacefully raised, chiefly on a diet of house rats from a neighborhood dump.

The voice of the great horned owl is the voice of the wilderness. Its basic phrase is a low, deep "hooo ho-hoo" or "hooo ho-ho-ho", repeated once or twice. I have heard it in many places, but it brings most vividly to mind the misty daybreak in Florida piney woods in October and November when the deep-voiced female and the higher-voiced males are calling. Then it is already nesting time there. In the northern states the great horned owl lays its eggs in an old crow's or a hawk's nest in February when snow still covers the ground, but in Florida its nests so early it lays its eggs in autumn or early winter. This gives the young the long summer to develop skill in hunting. The great horned owl, 22 inches long, is usually a buffy brown bird, but some are very pale, and others very dark.

BARRED OWL

A large, gray-brown owl with a round head and dark eyes, the barred owl (*Strix varia*) is a hoot owl, but unlike the great horned it speaks up loud and clear. In the north, from Nova Scotia to Yukon, it usually hoots "hoo hoo ho-ho hoo hoo ho-hoah," but in the southeastern wooded swamps, where the barred owl seems more common and more vocal, sometimes one hears a medley of "hoos" and "hoaws" even in the daytime. Though the hooting ushers in the nesting season when the owl usually chooses a hollow in a forest tree for a nest, later, after the young have flown, the birds may wander widely and their autumn hooting may be heard in shade trees of towns and villages. Compared with the great horned owl, the barred owl is less shy.

The barred owl is 21 inches long, has a barred breast and striped flanks, and its range is the eastern two thirds of the country in forest and woodlot. Its major food consists of small mammals.

The related spotted owl (*Strix occidentalis*) of the forests of the Far West has the whole underparts barred. The great gray owl (*Strix nebulosa*) is large, 29 inches long, and has yellow eyes.

Top: Elf owl (Microthene whitneyi)
Bottom: Burrowing owl (Speotyto cunicularia)

PYGMY OWL

Unlike most owls, the tiny, slim pygmy owl (*Glaucidium gnoma*) of the western forests is active by day. It perches in bushes and trees, watching for its prey, which includes more birds than other owls eat, and large prey considering its own small size. Its call, well known in its haunts, is a single whistled note repeated over and over, a call that is easily imitated and will attract not only pygmy owls but also many other small birds accustomed to scolding this predator. As with many small owls, the nest often is in an old woodpecker hole. It is 7 inches long, has a small, round head, a long tail and black streaks on the flanks. The closely related ferruginous owl (*Glaucidium brasilianum*) of South America ranges north only to the Mexican border country. The elf owl (*Micrathene whitneyi*), 6 inches long, and our smallest owl, has a short tail and mottled flanks. It ranges from Mexico north to the adjacent states for the summer.

BURROWING OWL

The burrowing owl (*Speotyto cunicularia*) is a most unusual owl, making its home in a burrow in grass country and sitting on the mound at the burrow's mouth during the day. This owl has a very short tail, is only 9 inches long, and has long, nearly bare legs. When approached it may bob and bow its round head and plump body before withdrawing into its burrow with a cackling call, or it may fly a short distance to perch on a fence post or other lookout. In the West the burrow is usually taken over from some ground squirrel or other digging rodent, but in Florida it digs its own. At the end of the 5 to 10-foot burrow the six white eggs are laid and the young raised mostly on large insects. The burrowing owl ranges from South America north to central Florida and the grasslands of the western United States. Though it prefers undisturbed prairie, I found it common in the irrigated cropland about El Centro in the Imperial Valley of California and it even nests on the Miami Airport.

OTHER OWLS

The snowy owl (*Nyctea scandiaca*), 25 inches long, nests on the Arctic tundra and during some winters numbers of them move south to grasslands and marshes of the northern states. The hawk owl (*Surnia ulula*), 15 inches long, nests in the boreal forests but sometimes its winter flight brings it to the northern states. The saw-whet owl (*Aegolius acadicus*), 8

Saw-whet owl (*Aegolius acadicus*)

inches long, nests across the continent in northern coniferous forests and migrates south in winter when individuals are occasionally found in towns and picked up by hand. The boreal owl (*Aegolius funereus*), 10 inches long, is another boreal forest bird but it rarely moves southward into settled areas. The long-eared owl (*Asio otus*), 16 inches long, is a forest bird of the temperate zone woodlands across the continent. The short-eared owl (*Asio flammeus*), 15 inches long, nests on the barrens and grasslands from the Arctic to the northern states and winters over much of the United States in grasslands, fields and marshes.

Goatsuckers and Nighthawks
(*Family Caprimulgidae*)

It is interesting to note how slight a clue can identify a bird. A telephone caller one day asked: "What is the brown bird that sits with its stomach on the ground, has a big mouth and whiskers like a catfish?" Obviously it was a whippoorwill. The six birds of this family in the United States are brown with a variegated owl-like pattern, very small feet, very small bill but with a very wide gape, and three of them have long bristles fringing the corner of the mouth.

All these birds have long wings and catch insects, large and small, in flight. The night hawks forage by day as well as night; the other species are nocturnal and are better known for the loud calls in which they repeat their names over and over. The two eggs are laid on the ground and the downy young are fed there or nearby until they can fly. The poor-will hibernates; all the other species are migratory.

CHUCK-WILL'S-WIDOW,
WHIPPOORWILL, AND THEIR KIN

From the time the chuck-will's-widow (*Caprimulgus carolinensis*) arrive from the tropics in early spring until the eggs hatch, its calls are as much a part of the Deep South night-time atmosphere as is the song of the mockingbird and the scent of jasmine. "Chuck will's wid-ow" says the bird calling it out scores and hundreds of times. Everyone hears the voice of the chuck-will's-widow but few see the bird for it sleeps away the da

148

perched lengthwise on a branch in some dark and shady patch of forest.

The chuck-will's-widow, 12 inches long, is clad in variegated dead-leaf tones of brown. It summers in the eastern half of the country north to Maryland and winters in South America. The whippoorwill (*Caprimulgus vociferus*), 10 inches long, is a more northern representative of the chuck-will's-widow, and best known for its oft repeated call, "whip-poor-will." The poor-will (*Phalaenoptilus nuttallii*) of the West is a still smaller bird, 7½ inches long, and grayer in color, and its call is "poor-will-ee." Yet another nightjar, the pauraque (*Nyctidromus albicollis*), 12 inches long, ranges from Mexico to south Texas.

COMMON NIGHTHAWK

The common nighthawk (*Chordeiles minor*) is associated in my mind with schoolhouses, for in many small towns it is the schoolhouse with its flat tar and gravel roof that nighthawks use for a nest site as readily as any stretch of bare earth or gravel in open country. The nighthawk commonly feeds by day as well as by night, over town and country, scooping up flying insects in its wide gape. In the spring it calls attention to itself with its hoarse "peent". About the nest the male also produces a booming sound resulting from the air that passes through its wings at the end of the display dive it makes for the benefit of the female.

In the Midwest I have watched continual irregular streams of migrating birds feeding in leisurely fashion as they flew southward low over the fields. One evening a few dozen birds lingered over an insect-rich pond in which the birds' reflections, approaching and retreating from each other, presented the graceful pattern of a dance.

The common nighthawk, 10 inches long, has gray-brown plumage and a white bar in each wing. It nests widely in North America. The related lesser nighthawk (*Chordeiles acutipennis*), 9 inches long, has a trilled call and occurs in summer in the West.

Swifts (*Family Apodidae*)

Many summers I have watched swifts course back and forth across the sky but I have never seen one alight. Once away from the chimney, hollow tree or rock crevice where they sleep or nest, they stay awing, collecting their insect food as they fly. I have even seen chimney swifts collect nest material by snatching dead twigs from treetops in their feet without a pause in their flight. With long narrow wings, small bill but wide gape and tiny feet, swifts recall swallows in appearance, but the swifts' flight seems to have a more hurried beat.

A body shaped like a cigar or a bow and arrow are the conventional but apt phrases used to describe what the blackish chimney swift (*Chaetura pelagica*) looks like as it dashes across the summer sky. Sometimes the wings appear to be beating alternately instead of simultaneously; but this is apparently an optical illusion probably created by an irregularity in the wing beat which serves to steer the bird, the spiny-tipped tail being evidently too short to serve as an effective rudder. Sometimes these swifts sail in twos or threes with wings held high, and their chattering, twittering notes come plainly to earth.

Where once the chimney swift nested in a hollow tree over much of the eastern United States, it now nests and roosts in chimneys. The nest is a half-saucer-shaped structure of twigs glued together and stuck to the wall of the chimney by a secretion of the salivary glands. Four or five white eggs are laid, and the young are cared for in the chimney by both parent until they can accompany the parents in rapid flight.

In late summer and early autumn the chimney swifts gather in the scores hundreds and thousands to roost in chimneys. This going to roost is a lengthy process. As the flock swirls around the chimney, a few individual drop in while the rest scatter, speed away and come back and re-form their funnel of moving birds. This takes place time after time. Finally just at dusk, the whole funnel starts down the chimney and in a matter of moments the bulk of the birds have disappeared. Inside they find place to cling, head up, breast to the wall and spiny tail braced for support Thus they spend the night.

A few nights later the roosting is over. The birds set off for their winter home in the upper Amazon Valley where they will revert to their ancient pattern of sleeping in hollow trees. The chimney swift is 5½ inches long and sooty black. The Vaux's swift (*Chaetura vauxi*) is the slightly smaller and paler far western counterpart of the chimney swift. It still nests in hollow trees and lives in wilderness conditions.

There are two other, rather different swifts in the western United States

The white-throated swift (*Aeronautes saxatalis*), 7 inches long, with much white in throat, center of breast and flanks, is a common bird of arid, rugged country. It sleeps and nests in small colonies in rock crevices and most of the birds go to Mexico and Central America for the winter.

The western black swift (*Cypseloides niger*), 7½ inches long, the largest American swift, is black with a little white in its forehead and has a slightly forked tail. This swift nests in deep moist crevices of mountain and sea cliffs, sometimes placing the nest behind a waterfall. It winters in tropical America.

Hummingbirds (*Family Trochilidae*)

Hummingbirds are small enough for hawk moths to be mistaken for them. They go from flower to flower, flying backward and forward with equal facility and probing each blossom for nectar and tiny insects. As they move about, their wings beat so rapidly that they blur and give off a buzzing or a humming sound. Hummingbirds have long, narrow wings and tiny feet that are used only for perching. Their special equipment for tapping the honey supply of flowers is the long, needle-like bill and nectar-sipping tongue. Hummingbirds do not depend entirely on flower feeding. I have seen them searching the bark of tree trunks and foliage, darting out to catch insects on the wing and flying back and forth through swarms of gnats.

At nesting time the male selects one or several exposed perches where he spends much time and makes display flights. There is no forming of pairs and the family cares are all borne by the female. She makes a nest out of a little cup of down saddled on a branch and camouflaged with lichen and spider web. Two tiny white eggs are laid in it, and the young are fed by regurgitation and are cared for in the nest until they fly. Almost all the American hummingbirds are migratory. Iridescent greens and blues with iridescent patches of red or purple on the head or throat of the male are common colors.

The American tropics is the headquarters of the large hummingbird family with fifteen species, ranging from 3 to 5 inches long, as part of the avifauna of the United States. In the East only one species occurs; in the

West are seven species, and seven more in the Mexican border country.

RUBY-THROATED HUMMINGBIRD

From their winter quarters in Central America some of the ruby-throated hummingbirds (*Archilochus colubris*) fly north across the Gulf of Mexico. Early March sees the birds on the north Gulf coast; in May they are in central Canada. In Ottawa, Ontario they arrive in numbers when the horse chestnut trees are white with spiked blooms. The birds are darting at and chasing each other with tiny squeaks; probing into flowers, and resting quietly on perches within the tree. The excited activity makes a count impossible but there must be dozens of birds. Some observers have suggested that there is a segregation of the sexes at this time.

When breeding starts the male often sits on a twig with a commanding view. A pugnacious sprite, he may dart off to chase a kingbird or crow or a rival male. His display is to make a pendulum-like flight back and forth in front of a female, inconspicuous in the shrubbery. She makes her nest in some hardwood tree or shrub and forages at a wide variety of flowers for food for her young, as well as scrutinizing tree trunks and foliage. Once I watched a female forage over the window of a shed, paying especial attention to the corners and edges of the glass where spiders' webs had accumulated. I was close enough to see her tongue flick out to secure what I supposed were tiny spiders and flies from the webs.

In September, migration is well under way and an account from Point Pelee on Lake Erie tells of the swarming, twittering ruby throats in a yellow-flowered mass of jewelweed and of individual birds taking off to fly south, low across the lake. Most of these birds go to Central America but a few in the Gulf of Mexico area. The ruby-throated hummingbird, 3½ inches ling, has glossy green upperparts, white underparts and in the male, an iridescent throat gorget that glows ruby red in the sunlight. Its summer range is in forest edge, shade trees and garden shrubbery in the eastern United States and Canada, where it is the only hummingbird.

ANNA'S HUMMINGBIRD

The Anna's hummingbird (*Calypte anna*) is the common hummingbird of California gardens. Otherwise it lives in stands of live oak and shrubbery on the lower mountain slopes and in canyons. Though a permanent resi-

Costa's hummingbird (Calypte costae)

dent, its shifts in foraging areas follow the seasonal succession of the blooming of plants.

This hummingbird seeks out the earliest native flowering shrubs such as manzanita and gooseberry of the slopes, then the currants and then a whole array of nectar-rich blooms until the sticky monkey flower blooms in August. Then individuals go into the stubble fields in September for blue curls or camphor weed. There is little native blooming in the period from October to January and the birds have profited by the introduced plants that bloom then, especially the redhotpoker plant in northern California and the tobacco tree in southern California. Other favorites for feeding and for nesting are the many varieties of eucalyptus trees.

The males of many hummingbirds give a display flight, and that of the Anna's hummingbird is one of the most spectacular. Starting from a point 60 to 100 feet above a female feeding or perching in the shrubbery, the male makes a power dive toward her at a speed that perhaps approaches 60 miles an hour. Reaching the level of the female he pulls out of the dive with an explosive whistling chip. Then, for a few seconds he hovers in the air over the female, body horizontal, giving a squeaky song before flying straight up, with his body still horizontal, to repeat the dive. The nesting season begins early in September and is prolonged for months, perhaps because more than one brood is raised in a year.

The Anna's hummingbird, 4 inches long, is green above, white below, with a red throat and red crown in the male, and is a permanent resident of western California.

OTHER WESTERN HUMMINGBIRDS

The rufous hummingbird (*Selasphorus rufus*) nests further north than any other species, summering from the State of Washington to Alaska. In its northern spring migrations through the lowlands of California the birds swarm in the blossoming orange and peach orchards. Their southward migration in July and August takes a different route farther east, following the crests of the mountains as far east as Colorado and New Mexico, to profit by the late blooming flowers there. The rufous hummingbird, 3½ inches long, is mostly rufous brown with a green crown. The Allen's hummingbird (*Selasphorus sasin*), 3½ inches long, is like the rufous hummingbird but with a green back. It summers in moist shrubbery, forest edge and gardens of coastal California. The black-chinned humming-

Top: Anna's hummingbird (Calypte anna)
Bottom: Ruby-throated hummingbird (Archilochus colubris)

bird (*Archilochus alexandri*), 3½ inches long, is the western counterpart of the ruby-throated hummingbird but has a black chin. It summers in stands of deciduous trees and shrubs along streams and canyons and in orchards.

The Calliope hummingbird (*Stellula calliope*), 3 inches long, is our smallest hummingbird and has a violet and white-streaked gorget with elongated corners. It is a common breeding species of coniferous forest glades of the western mountains. The broad-tailed hummingbird (*Selasphorus platycercus*) is similar to the ruby-throated hummingbird of the East but in its green upperparts and red throat is unlike any other western species. Common in the Rocky Mountains at higher altitudes, the broadtail summers where the forests give way to shrubs along glades, mountain meadows and streams. Its nest is identical to that of the rufous hummingbird, and is often placed on a small limb over running water. The tiny Costa's hummingbird (*Calypte costae*), 3½ inches long, is unique in having a violet crown and throat with elongate corners to the gorget. Its summer home is in the shrubby deserts of the West where cactus, mesquite and sage grow and it is the only common hummingbird there.

HUMMINGBIRDS OF THE MEXICAN BORDER

The seven species of Mexican hummingbirds that extend their ranges north only into the Texas-south Arizona area are as follows: the tiny lucifer hummingbird (*Calothorax lucifer*), 3¼ inches long, has a deeply forked tail, a downcurved bill and a violet gorget with elongated corners. The large Rivoli's hummingbird (*Eugenes fulgens*), 5 inches long, is a dark bird with a green gorget, a purple crown and a tiny white mark back of the eye. The similar blue-throated hummingbird (*Lampornis clemenciae*), 5 inches long, has a blue throat, green crown and two narrow white lines in the face and broadly white-tipped outer tail feathers. The much smaller broad-billed hummingbird (*Cynanthus latirostris*), 3 ¾ inches long, is a dark green and blue bird with a red bill. The white-eared hummingbird (*Hylocharis leucotis*) is similar but with a conspicuous white streak back of the eye. Quite different are the medium-sized, buff-bellied hummingbird (*Amazilia yucatanensis*), 4 ½ inches long, with a red bill, brown tail and buffy brown underparts except for the green throat, and the violet-crowned hummingbird (*Amazilia verticalis*), 4½ inches long, which has a black bill and the underparts white from chin to belly.

Trogons *(Family Trogonidae)*

The coppery-tailed trogon *(Trogon elegans)* is a quietly elegant bird of Central America that reaches the United States only in the mountains of the Mexican border country. There it lives in the oak and pine slopes and the sycamore and oak canyons of the mountains along with such other Mexican birds as the Harlequin quail, the whiskered owl, the violet-crowned hummingbird, the rose-breasted becard and the red-fronted warbler. I know this trogon only from Salvador where it was common in tall second growth and forest and where it preferred shady places and sat quietly upright on a branch with its tail straight down. From there it flew out to snap up insects in the air or from leaf or twig; it plucked berries in the same way. Its call was a loud, hoarse "koa" repeated a number of times and it also gave a series of low hooting calls. Its nest is in a hole in a tree and there it raises its young. About 12 inches long, the male has a red

Young belted kingfishers (Megaceryle alcyon)

breast and belly and coppery green throat and back. It belongs to a tropical family with only one species in the United States.

Kingfishers *(Family Alcedinidae)*

The belted kingfisher *(Megaceryle alcyon)* is a blue and white bird of bold outline. His large bill, jagged crest on his big head, tiny feet and short tail give the impression of being cut out with a jigsaw, and his loud rattling call of alarm sounds as if from a wooden noisemaker. A stub, a bare branch, a wire from which there is a view into the water of lake, stream or canal, is this solitary fisher's perch. From these, like a hurled, dagger-tipped projectile, he plunges into the water for the fish that comes into view. The kingfisher may go completely underwater but rises at once, fish gripped in its bill, and flies to a perch where the prey, if unruly, is beaten into submission and swallowed. Sometimes the intended prey darts out of sight and then the kingfisher checks its dive and with fanning, white-speckled wings hovers in the air, watching it. Belted kingfishers breed over much of the United States wherever there are fish-rich waters with suitable perches and cutbanks; in these the pair digs a deep tunnel with an enlarged chamber at the end. Here the five to eight white eggs are laid and the naked, helpless young hatch and grow into facsimiles of their parents—13 inches long, the males with one blue breast band, the females with a blue and rufous one.

When northern waters freeze, some kingfishers move south, and locally in the Southeast solitary birds perched on telephone wires by roadside canals are common and conspicuous. Some birds, however, are amazingly hardy, lingering in the north by open water of coast and open pools. One of the several tropical kingfishers, the green kingfisher *(Chloroceryle americana),* occurs along streams in the Mexican border country.

Woodpeckers *(Family Picidae)*

Digging insects out of solid wood is orthodox woodpecker behavior, for which they are especially adapted, and some, such as the downy woodpecker, get much of their food this way. But many woodpeckers also use other, less laborious ways of feeding, taking insects from the air, leaves and ground, and eating nuts, berries and fruits. A rolling tattoo drummed out on a resonant dead limb or tin roof is used to supplement the springtime calls in the early stages of establishment of territory and getting a mate. All of the woodpeckers, however, chisel a flask-shaped cavity in a tree trunk for a nest; there they lay their white eggs on the chip-lined floor and both parents care for their young. Some woodpeckers are migratory; others are largely permanent residents.

In the United States there are twenty-three woodpeckers, ranging from 6 to 20 inches long.

DOWNY WOODPECKER

Ornithologists from the time of Audubon have been impressed by the industry and the diligence of the downy woodpecker (*Dendrocopos pubescens*) in carrying out its feeding behavior. It hitches up a tree trunk head first by a series of hops, poking under a flake of bark, looking into a crevice and tapping here and there. A likely spot is chosen for excavation, perhaps because it sounds different when tapped, perhaps because the bird's hearing tells of an insect stirring in its tunnel. Then, head up, spine-tipped tail braced, the bird pounds out chips with its chisel-shaped bill until a grub's tunnel is broken into; the woodpecker's long, barbed tongue is then pushed in to entangle and withdraw the insect. Then the bird continues its search out onto slender branches. When insects are abundant during the summer some are taken from twig and leaf; when berries and nuts are ripe they are not completely ingored; and when winter comes a downy woodpecker often is one of the most faithful visitors to the suet at feeding stations. Outside the breeding season the downy is extremely pugnacious towards others of its kind, but strangely a lone bird will often join a band of foraging chickadees.

The downy woodpecker, 6 inches long, and its larger relative, the hairy woodpecker (*Dendrocopos villosus*), 9 inches long, share the distinction of having the widest range, occurring summer and winter almost wherever there are trees in the United States. These birds are black and white with a white stripe down the middle of the back. There are several related species in various parts of the country. In the mature pine stands of the southeastern states lives the red-cocaded woodpecker (*Dendrocopos borea-*

lis), with its black and white barred back; in the southwestern states is the ladder-backed woodpecker (*Dendrocopos scalaris*), the male with a red crown; in California west of the Sierras is the Nuttall's woodpecker (*Dendrocopos nuttallii*) with much black in its face; and in the mountain forests of southern Arizona and New Mexico lives the Arizona woodpecker (*Dendrocopos arizonae*) with a brown back but without conspicuous white. A differently colored relative is the white-headed woodpecker (*Dendrocopos albolarvatus*) of the mountains of the West; it has a black back and breast and white head and throat.

PILEATED AND IVORY-BILLED WOODPECKERS

When pioneering man with his lumbering, frontier farming and his sustenance hunting first entered an area it was a sad day for large, conspicuous and edible birds such as the pileated woodpecker (*Dryocopus pileatus*) and the ivory-billed woodpecker (*Campephilus principalis*). They retreated before the first impact of civilization. But, as the logging camps moved on and saplings grew to second growth and later forest, as marginal and submarginal farm land was abandoned and exploitation and vandalism of wild life gave way to a different attitude, one in which there was an appreciation of the whole environment and a desire to protect and maintain its threatened elements, a new era came. The pileated woodpecker was able to take advantage of this trend and has recolonized many areas from which it had been driven out. Seldom do I make a long auto drive in the southeastern states today without seeing at least one of these birds from the road. The ivory-billed woodpecker has not the resilience of the pileated nor its adaptability. It has steadily retreated—from Florida and from the Carolinas and Louisiana, the most recent records there being decades old. The only locality where it is surely known to survive is the Big Thicket country of Texas.

The pileated woodpecker, 18 inches long, has a solid black back. It is a permanent resident of the forests of the eastern United States and ranges north of the plains to the Pacific coast. Much of its food is secured in usual woodpecker fashion. The ivory-billed, 20 inches long, shows much white in the back and in the folded wing. It is threatened with extinction. A critical need of the species seems to be newly dead, old forest trees from which it can scale the bark in search of its favorite food, large grubs living under the bark.

160

RED-HEADED AND ACORN WOODPECKERS

Though the red-headed woodpecker (*Melanerpes erythrocephalus*) of the eastern half of the United States sometimes feeds in orthodox woodpecker fashion, chiseling wood-boring insects from tree trunks, it often behaves otherwise. Along country roads I have often seen them perched on a fence post or on a telephone wire, watching for insects which they fly out to catch on the wing, or down and take on the ground or on the road. This last habit has exposed the species to a new danger and it is common to find one flattened by automobiles. In the autumn the red-head feeds on berries and fruit, and picks acorns and wedges them into holes or cracks in tree trunks where they are held as in a vise and hammered to pieces. In some areas corn left in the field near woodlots is a staple winter food and is processed like the acorns. The fluctuation in populations is very marked some years, possibly being correlated with fluctuations in the crops of acorns and beechnuts.

It is, however, the related acorn woodpecker (*Melanerpes formicivorus*) of the oak groves of the Far West and Southwest that has specialized in acorns and has developed the habit of drilling holes in the bark of pine, oak and sycamore, and fitting an acorn into each hole. An observer counted 60 acorns thus stored in a space 5 inches wide and 2 feet long, and estimated 50,000 acorns stored in the trunk of one great pine. It is this stored food that carries the bird over the winter. When there is a failure of the acorn crop, the bird may store pebbles, a curious miscarriage of instinct. A lack of food leads to local movements of populations. In summer the acorn woodpecker may feed on insects, like the red-headed woodpecker.

The red-headed woodpecker, 10 inches long, has a red head and neck and most of its plumage is a boldly patterned black and white. The related acorn woodpecker, 9 inches long, is more black than white and has a red crown and a curious pattern of white on its forehead, cheeks and throat.

FLICKERS

The yellow-shafted flicker (*Colaptes auratus*), 13 inches long, is the woodpecker that alights on lawns, looks around, hops or runs a few paces and repeats. He is searching for ant hills. He is generally an olive brown bird but when he flies the yellow of wing and tail and the great white rump patch give a strikingly different pattern. He flies to perch on a post or tree trunk and in the spring his calls, including "wicker..." are noisy but pleasing, and on tree trunk or branch two birds may display with spread wings and tails and a swaying of the head and body. With a strong preference for village and rural areas, it is a well-known and well-liked bird. This flicker also nests in scantily wooded areas, including the trees fringing prairie rivers, around homesteads and on the edges of forest where the birds have ready access to open ground. The range of the yellow-shafted flicker is the eastern half of the United States and in Canada northwest to Alaska. Northern birds withdraw southward in winter and then may feed on fruits, berries and even such dry food as sumac berries.

The red-shafted flicker (*Colaptes cafer*) of the West, also 13 inches long, has, as the name implies, red instead of yellow in wing and tail and where its range meets that of the yellow-shaft, **northwest of the plains**, extensive hybridization occurs. A third, smaller **species, the** gilded flicker (*Colaptes chrysoides*), 11 inches long and **with yellow** in wings and tail, lives in the shrubby deserts of the Southwest where its nest holes are conspicuous in the saguaro cactus.

OTHER WOODPECKERS

There are three medium-sized woodpeckers, 9-10 inches long, that have the whole back barred black and white and the underparts whitish, pinkish or buffy and are common, conspicuous birds in their respective ranges. These woodpeckers eat a great deal of fruit. They are the red-bellied woodpecker (*Centurus carolinus*) of the eastern half of the United States, the golden fronted woodpecker (*Centurus aurifrons*) of Texas and Mexico, and the gila woodpecker (*Centurus uropygialis*) of the western deserts.

The other woodpeckers fall into three groups: sapsuckers; the two species of three-toed woodpeckers; and the Lewis woodpecker. The sapsuckers have adapted to tapping trees for their sap, which, with the inner layer of bark and some insects and fruit, forms their diet. They migrate in winter. There are two species, the first, the yellow-bellied sapsucker (*Sphyrapicus varius*), 8½ inches long, rather remarkable for the difference in color and pattern between the eastern and the western subspecies. This bird lives in the spruce and aspen of the northern forests across the continent. The second species is the Williamson's sapsucker (*Sphyrapicus thyroideus*), 9½ inches long, which is remarkable for the difference between the male and the female. This species nests in the mountains of the West in the coniferous forests at higher altitudes.

162   *Pileated woodpecker (Dryocopus pileatus*

In the boreal coniferous forests of the north and western mountains live two dark woodpeckers whose flanks are barred with black and white. The males have yellow crowns. One, the black-backed three-toed woodpecker (*Picoides arcticus*), 9 inches long, feeds frequently by knocking flakes of bark from dead pines and spruces to get insects. The northern three-toed woodpecker (*Picoides tridactylus*), 8½ inches long, has a black and white barred back. Both species are permanent residents.

The Lewis woodpecker (*Asyndesmus lewis*), 11 inches long, of the western mountains, is black with a pink belly, a gray collar and a red face. It eats nuts, fruits, and insects and assembles in flocks in the autumn.

Cotingas *(Family Cotingidae)*

The cotinga family is a large tropical American family with such notable members as the vivid orange cock-of-the-rock, the umbrella-crested umbrella bird, and the loud-voiced bell-bird. Only a single cotinga reaches the United States, the rose-throated becard (*Platypsaris aglaiae*), which reaches its farthest north in southern Arizona and Texas, where it is rare and local in occurrence. The becard, about 6½ inches long, is an undistinguished bird, the male gray with a dusky cap and a red throat patch, the female buffy and brown with a black cap. Related to the flycatchers, the becard has some of the flycatcher habits, sitting quietly high in the trees and darting out after flying insects, but it varies this with plucking insects from leaf and twig and by eating berries. The most remarkable feature of the becard is its nest, a domed, oval structure as big as a football, dangling from a high branch of a tree. The entrance is at the side and the four to six eggs are white with brown markings. The presence of old nests has been the first indication found of the occurrence of the bird in some areas.

Tyrant Flycatchers *(Family Tyrannidae)*

One August a southbound migrant wood pewee perched upright on the telephone wire above our garden. Ignoring us, it sat quietly except for occasional sallies to snap up passing insects. It was not a likely candidate for hand feeding. But when I picked an insect from the grape arbor and flicked it into the air the pewee darted out and snapped it up. This was repeated several times until, apparently satiated, the bird went to sleep. This illustrates not only the flycatching habit of the family but the indifference of most of these flycatchers to man if he keeps a proper distance. The pugnacity, another characteristic of the tyrant flycatchers, was illustrated by a kingbird sitting on a wire near an inoffensive upland plover that was upset about its young. As the plover flew near the kingbird it darted out and knocked a tuft of feathers from the plover's back.

The flycatcher family, which is strictly American, has 365 species and has its headquarters in the tropics. The 32 species occurring in the United States and Canada are small to medium-sized perching birds 5 to 10 inches long except for the 17-inch scissor-tailed flycatcher. Most species are dull or plain colored in both sexes but the vermillion flycatcher and the scissor-tailed flycatcher are notable exceptions. Though flying insects are their chief diet, some berries are eaten in season. The voices of some species are harsh, of others musical, but song is not well developed. The nest is usually cup-shaped and placed in a bush or tree and the two to six eggs white with or without dark markings. Migration is usual in this group and some species move as far south as South America in winter.

The arrangement of the species is: kingbirds, scissor-tailed flycatcher, crested flycatchers, phoebes, empidonax flycatchers, wood pewees, olive-sided flycatcher, vermillion flycatcher and tropical flycatchers of the Mexican border.

KINGBIRDS

An eastern kingbird (*Tyrannus tyrannus*) in hot pursuit of a passing crow is a common sight in the northeastern states. Many birds defend nesting territories but the kingbird has an extra measure of pugnacity. Not only does it fiercely attack potential predators but it is equally violent in attacking such harmless birds as doves and upland plovers. Nor does the pugnacity disappear with the end of the breeding season: I have seen a migrating kingbird dive at a passing little green heron.

The eastern kingbird's favorite habitat includes scattered trees and open spaces such as farmlands in eastern Canada, wolf willow clumps and lines of poplars on the prairies and open pine lands in the gulf states. The trees

Overleaf: Top left: Red-headed woodpecker (Melanerpes erythrocephalus)
Bottom left: Yellow-bellied sapsucker (Sphyrapicus varius)
Right: Yellow-shafted flicker (Colaptes auratus)

provide nesting places and along with fence posts and wires furnish perches from which to watch over the fields for prey. Small and medium-sized insects are usually taken on the wing but the size of large grasshoppers that can be crammed into the gaping maws of hungry fledglings is surprising. Like so many insect-eating birds, kingbirds may eat berries in the autumn, usually hovering in front of the twig to pluck the fruit. Migration begins early in September and loose parties of the birds move southward to their winter quarters in South America.

The eastern kingbird is one of six related species of regular occurrence. They are large flycatchers, 8 to 9 inches long, that sit up on exposed perches on trees or shrubs in open or semi-open country and fly out to snap up insects in flight. The nest is a basin-shaped structure in a low tree. The eastern kingbird summers across the country except for the Far West and Southwest and has grayish black upperparts, white underparts and a white tip to its black tail. The western kingbird (*Tyrannus verticalis*) also has a wide summer range in the western half of the country and straggles to the

Scissor-tailed flycatcher (*Muscivora forficata*)

eastern states. It is gray above with white throat, dull yellow breast and the white outer tail feathers contrast with an otherwise black tail.

The other four kingbirds are of more limited distribution: the Cassin's kingbird (*Tyrannus vociferans*) of the Southwest, where some are permanent residents, is like the western kingbird but darker and lacks the white outer tail feathers. The tropical kingbird (*Tyrannus melancholicus*) of limited occurrence along the Mexican border has a bright yellow breast and belly. The gray kingbird (*Tyrannus dominicensis*) of coastal Florida is like the eastern kingbird but its upperparts are paler gray and the tail lacks a white tip. The thick-billed kingbird (*Tyrannus crassirostris*) of the mountains of the Mexican border has brownish upperparts and the white underparts tinged yellow on the abdomen.

SCISSOR-TAILED FLYCATCHER

A slender, gray and black kingbird with pink flanks and a very long tail is the impresion one gets of the scisor-tailed flycatcher (*Muscivora forficata*) sitting quietly on a fence post or a bush in the open country of Texas and Oklahoma. How different the bird looks when making quick turns in pursuit of an insect or in the aerial antics of the display flight! Then the salmon and red underwing flashes out and the very long deeply forked tail spreads to show pink, white and black. The nest is usually built in a shrub or small tree. In the autumn the birds gather in flocks and move southward to winter in Central America.

CRESTED FLYCATCHERS

The great crested flycatcher (*Myiarchus crinitus*) arrives in the spring to live in the hardwood and pine forests of the eastern part of the country where it has favorite perches well up in the canopy. He announces his presence with flashing of red-brown wings and tail and a series of noisy calls, the most conspicuous of which I think of as a screech, but he also has whistled notes, all of which tend to be emphatic and ear-catching. The bird is as big as a kingbird and like it has a large share of intolerance toward birds of about its size or smaller and even towards squirrels. But unlike the kingbird the crested flycatcher usually does not chase hawks or crows.

The nest, unlike that of most flycatchers, is placed by preference in a natural hole or a crevice in a tree trunk. If the cavity is large a considerable mass of twigs, leaves and moss may be used to fill up the unwanted space

before the nest proper is lined with finer material. A striking feature of the nests is that almost always there is some shed snake skin added, a trait for which folklore writers have provided improbable explanations. While a few great crested flycatchers may winter in the southern states the main wintering grounds are from Mexico to northern South America.

The great crested flycatcher and its three near relatives have a more upright posture and are more noisy than most flycatchers. Although called "crested," "bushy headed" is more accurate for the "crest" is, for instance, nothing like the pointed crest of a blue jay. The four crested flycatchers range from 7 to 9 inches long and have olive heads and backs, gray throats, yellow or yellowish abdomens and two wing bars. The wings and tails are conspicuous rufous brown except in the smallest species. All tend to be forest or brushland birds and all build their nests in cavities or crevices, either natural or made by woodpeckers.

The great crested flycatcher (*Myiarchus crinitus*) of the eastern half of the country is large and brightly colored. The Wied's crested flycatcher (*Myiarchus tyrannulus*) of limited distribution in the Southwest is also large but paler than the great crested flycatcher. The ash-throated flycatcher (*Myiarchus cinerascens*) common in the West and Southwest in oaks, sage-brush and cactus desert shrubbery is medium sized and darker than the above two species. The olivaceous flycatcher (*Myiarchus tuberculifer*) of the Mexican border country of the Southwest is the smallest and the darkest species, being 7 inches long and with little rufous in the brown of wing and tail.

PHOEBES

The three species of phoebes are medium-sized flycatchers, 6-8 inches long, that lack conspicuous wing bars in adult plumage and also lack eye rings. A striking behavioral pattern is that of twitching the tail downward. The nest is also distinctive, being built in a sheltered place: on or against a bank, cliff, or man-made structure. The eastern phoebe (*Sayornis phoebe*) of the eastern half of the country is gray above with blackish head, wings and tail. The black phoebe (*Sayornis nigricans*) of the Southwest is black with white lower breast and abdomen. The Say's phoebe (*Sayornis saya*), widespread in the west from Alaska to Mexico, is grayish brown on the back with head, wings and tail darker, and rusty brown on the underparts.

Modest in plumage and unobtrusive in behavior, the eastern phoebe has

Top: Crested flycatcher (Myiarchus crinitus)
Bottom: Eastern phoebe (Sayornis phoebe)

a distinctive but not loud song of "phoebe" or "feebee" that announces its name. It is an undemanding associate of rural man, nesting on farm buildings, sheds or cottages and under bridges where mud for the base of its nest and a sheltered ledge on which to place it are available. Originally the eastern phoebe must have been confined to rocky ravines and cliffs along streams for nest sites and it must be one of the birds that has benefited by the spread of settlement. Summering in the eastern part of the country and wintering in the Gulf states, eastern phoebes arrive early in March in various northern states and then can switch from their flycatcher habits to eating seeds and fruit to make survival possible when the weather is cold.

The black phoebe is the southwestern counterpart of the eastern phoebe. Water, ocean edge, stream, pond, irrigation ditch and even a watering trough for cattle may serve as sources of mud for use in their nests. Sheltered rock or wooden wall, sea bluff, canyon walls, bridges and buildings of town or ranch supply sheltered vertical faces against which to plaster their cup-shaped nests of mud. But the water's edge is attractive to the birds at all seasons; there they dart out for flying insects or pick floating insects from its surface. This habitat preference gives the black phoebe a scattered distribution in the generally arid and semi-arid Southwest and California but during rainy periods individuals wander and may colonize newly formed bodies of water.

Quite unlike the black phoebe in its choice of a nesting place, the Say's phoebe is a bird of open arid territory, the plains, badlands and rocky slopes of the West. It nests about ranch buildings and niches in rock walls and cut banks where there is a firm shelf for its nest.

EMPIDONAX FLYCATCHERS

Perhaps the most difficult task in American ornithology is to arrange the birds of this group into species. They are fairly easily recognized as belonging to the genus *Empidonax* on the basis of being small, big-headed flycatchers, 5 to 6 inches long, with upright posture and coloring in shades of olive, drab and gray and with whitish wing bars on their dark wings and pale eye rings. These flycatchers sit up within the foliage of tree or shrub and dart out after insects in the air or from leaves. The nest is usually cup-shaped and placed in a fork though one species nests on the ground and the 3 to 4 white eggs are white with or without spots. In winter, migration to warmer climates is the rule.

172

Dusky flycatcher (Empidonox oberholseri)

There are nine species of these perplexingly similar little flycatchers. Five are found only in the West, Hammond's (*Empidonax hammondii*), dusk (*Empidonax oberholseri*), gray (*Empidonax wrightii*), western (*Empidonax difficilis*), and buff-breasted flycatcher (*Empidonax fulvifrons*). Two summer only in the northern forest belt, the yellow-bellied (*Empidonax flavientris*) and the least flycatcher (*Empidonax minimus*). One is confined to the eastern woodlands, the Acadian flycatcher (*Empidonax virescens*), and one is more widespread in the brush and wooded areas across the central and northern part of the continent, the Traill's flycatcher (*Empidonax traillii*).

Many bird watchers are content to let these birds pass simply as Empidonax flycatchers, and in the autumn migrations when immature plumages complicate the picture this is certainly reasonable. On their breeding grounds, however, using geography, habitat, song and nest as well as appearance, it is possible for a competent observer to separate some with fair

173

assurance. For instance, the least flycatcher's "che-bek," the Acadian fly-catcher's semi-pensile nest slung in a flat fork, and the gray flycatcher's habitat of sage brush in the great basin, are all indications of identity. Only the buff-breasted flycatcher of the Southwest seems readily identified on its brownish-buff plumage. On the other hand, a recent authoritative bird guide says that the Hammond's flycatcher is often impossible to tell from the dusky flycatcher by sight or song.

A problem for taxonomists to classify, they are also a challenge to field biologists to discover how the birds tell each other apart. In fact, certain field biologists think one of the nine species listed here as currently accep-ted, the Traill's flycatcher, is really two species differing in type of song and nest.

WOOD PEWEES

The plaintive whistled "pee-wee," "pe-ah-whee" from the medium sized, rather nondescript flycatcher perched in the upper part of a tree tells one the bird is an eastern wood pewee (*Contopus virens*). It may interrupt its singing to make its characteristic long dash after some flying insect and then go back to its perch again. A clear view of the bird shows it to be a rather slender, brownish gray flycatcher with a whitish line down the center of the breast and two obscure wing bars. Although not distinguished in appearance, the wood pewee makes a beautifully dainty nest saddled on a horizontal branch and camouflaged with lichen on the outside so that it does not look like a nest at all, but part of the branch when seen from below.

The eastern wood pewee summers in wooded areas of the eastern part of the country and its place is taken in the West by the very similar western wood pewee (*Contopus sordidulus*), which, however, has a different, rasping voice. In the mountains of the Southwest lives a similar but larger wood pewee, 7½ inches long, called the Coues' flycatcher (*Contopus pertinax*).

OLIVE-SIDED FLYCATCHER

The olive-sided flycatcher (*Nuttallornis borealis*) is a bold bird that sits on the top of a spruce tree in plain sight and sings out, loud and clear, "whip-three-cheers" or "quick-three-beers". Its summer home is among the coni-fers of the North and West and its shallow, neat nest is placed on a flat branch among the twigs. A typical flycatcher, 7½ inches long, the olive-

174

sided is a rather short-tailed, big-headed, large-billed, brownish bird with some white in throat and breast and with vivid white flank patches that may show above the rump.

VERMILLION FLYCATCHERS

In the open shrubbery of the edge of the Arizona desert the male vermillion flycatcher's (*Pyrocephalus rubinus*) red crown and breast outshines the cactus and ocotillo blossoms and is so vivid that the brown of the back and face hardly registers. It is this red that one sees as the male flies up, circles and sails in the display flight. But what I found still more striking were the territorial disputes when two males sing and display, breast to breast, scarlet breast feathers puffed out and scarlet crest raised. There were occasional pauses for flycatching but the brown females who would nest in the nearby mesquite or cottonwood were rarely in evidence. The vermillion flycatcher is a more tropical species whose range in the United States is limited to the semi-arid desert shrubbery of the Southwest.

TROPICAL FLYCATCHERS OF THE MEXICAN BORDER

The kiskadee flycatcher (*Pitangus sulphuratus*), 10 inches long, with bright yellow underparts and crown, rufous rump and tail, and black and white side of the head, enters our area only in south Texas. The sulphur-bellied flycatcher (*Myiodynastes luteiventris*) 7-8 inches long with yellow, brown-streaked underparts and rufous tail reaches only to southern Arizona. The third species, the beardless flycatcher (*Camptostoma imberbe*), is notable only for being a curious grayish bird, 4½ inches long, with a small bill, no distinctive markings and often behaving like a vireo or titmouse. Its range is along the Mexican border in Arizona and Texas.

Larks (*Family Alaudidae*)

The lark of the poets is the skylark (*Alauda arvensis*) of Europe, noted for its flight song, which in North America can be heard only in grassland and pastures of southern Vancouver Island. There a colony of skylarks was introduced between 1902 and 1913; it is well established but has not extended its range. It is 7 inches long with a sparrowy streaked breast and back and a bill somewhat more slender than a sparrow's. The horned lark (*Eremophila alpestris*) of Eurasia and North America nests in wide expanses of barren country that have short sparse grasses; also on arctic tundra, some prairies, California deserts, salt marshes of the Texas coast and cultivated lands in the Midwest and the Northeast, before the grasses start to grow. The horned lark sometimes sings on the ground but it has a flight song similar to that of the skylark, given as the bird circles from 250 to 800 feet above the earth, repeating its thin, metallic twittering at intervals for several minutes before plunging back to earth. In winter, northern birds move south and the flocks feed in open country and shores of the oceans, often in company with longspurs. The horned lark, 7 inches long, is plain brown above, whitish or yellow tinged below and with a black and white pattern of forehead, cheeks and throat including small black tufts, the "horns," over each eye. The rest of the family, nearly a hundred species, live in the Old World. Larks walk on the ground, eat insects or seed in season, and the cup-shaped nest is placed on the ground.

Swallows (*Family Hirundinidae*)

One of my favorite places for swallow watching is a quiet pond where swarms of gnats rise in the evening and swallows gather to feed on them. Scores of these birds circle, swoop, cross and crisscross, check and change course to pursue an escaping insect or drop down to pick up a floating insect or take a sip of water. Other swallows line up on a nearby telephone wire and there is a continual coming and going of the birds.

Swallows are remarkably different from all other song birds in having short legs and tiny feet for perching quietly, long pointed wings for continuous active feeding on the wing, and a very small bill but a wide gape for catching flying insects. The family is nearly world-wide and there are eight species in North America. Although much alike in form and size, ranging from 5 to 8 inches long, their coloration permits ready identification of the adults. The greatest differences between many of the species are in the distinctive types of nesting. Five of our swallows may nest about man's homes and gardens, some in bird houses, their cheerful chattering, their graceful form and flight and flycatching habits making them welcome neighbors. When nesting is finished all eight species migrate, some as far as South America. Some swallows are colonial, others nest singly, but at migration time they may gather in great flocks to feed and to roost in trees or in reeds of marshes.

MUD-NEST SWALLOWS

There are two mud-nest swallows, the cliff swallow (*Petrochelidon pyrrhonota*) that nests on the outside of buildings and the barn swallow (*Hirundo rustica*) that nests inside barns, each swallow building up its nest with mouthful after mouthful of mud gathered from the edge of some puddle. The nesting on and in buildings is of course modern, a change from primitive nesting in rock crevices and on cliff faces, and this change has enabled these swallows to profit by settlement in America and to become much more widespread and common.

Aided by its long outer tail feathers the barn swallow is the fastest and

Barn swallow (Hirundo rustica)

most graceful bird in aerial maneuvers as it skims over meadow, pond or barn-yard. Its shallow nest of mud lined with feathers is placed on a beam in a barn or other outbuilding. In addition to the deeply forked tail of the adult the species is characterized by its rusty orange underparts and blue-black back and rump.

The cliff swallow by contrast has only the throat and breast rust colored and has a rusty brown rump and a square tail. Its nest is a flask-shaped structure plastered against a sheltered place on wall or cliff where rain will not reach it and the nests are often placed side by side in colonies of hundreds of birds. The related cave swallow (*Petrochelidon fulva*) of Mexico and south Texas makes a shelflike mud nest attached to the wall of a cave.

TREE-HOLE AND BIRD-BOX SWALLOWS

Three swallows originally made nests of straws and feathers in holes in trees. The tree swallow (*Iridoprocne bicolor*) and the violet green swallow (*Tachycineta thalassina*) still do so over much of their range but most purple martins (*Progne subis*) now nest in bird houses.

The tree swallow, with underparts white and upperparts glossy green and black, is not colonial but establishes a territory around its nest in a hole in a tree or in a single family bird house. This swallow is the first to arrive in the spring and the last to depart in the autumn. Indeed, it is the only swallow to winter regularly in the United States, where great flocks of them remain in Florida and violate swallow custom by feeding on myrtle berries. Still sensitive to cold, the tree swallows may congregate on a road in the early morning to warm themselves in the sun and suffer severe mortality from motor traffic. The tree swallow summers in the wooded northern areas across the continent. The related violet-green swallow (*Tachycineta thalassina*) summers in the West from California to Alaska.

The gurgling chatter of the nesting purple martin has a contented sound and is as much an attractive feature of having a martin colony in one's yard as is the sight of the birds' graceful forms soaring over the garden. Many martin houses have ten to thirty rooms but ones of hundreds have been made and Greggsville, Illinois has called itself the purple martin capital of the nation because of its abundant martin population.

Probably few people have seen purple martins nesting in such primitive quarters as a hole in a tree, but some martins still do so and in the Southeast

178

some still nest in primitive nest boxes, such as gourds with a hole cut in the side, which have been hung up for them. As a modern touch, white plastic bleach bottles are sometimes substituted for gourds. When nesting is over the martins gather in flocks, perch in long lines on wires and at night may fly to great roosts in trees where there may be many thousands of the birds. The purple martin is our largest swallow. The male is completely black with a purple gloss, the female duller and with a white belly.

BANK-NESTING SWALLOWS

Our smallest and dullest swallows are the bank and rough-winged swallows, with upperparts dark brownish and underparts mostly white, the bank swallow (*Riparia riparia*) with a distinct band across upper breast and the rough-winged swallow (*Stelgidopteryx ruficollis*) with a brownish throat and breast. Scores and even hundreds of tunnels are dug by the bank swallows into an earthen cut bank to house the nests of their colonies. The rough-winged swallows nest singly in burrows or in natural or man-made crevices or holes in banks. Both species summer across the continent and winter southward.

Crows and their Relatives (*Family Corvidae*)

Such phrases as "one crow sorrow," "as the crow flies," "chatter like a magpie," "naked as a jay bird" and "raven, bird of ill omen" from folk sayings and literature illustrate how the crows and their relatives are not only among the best known of our birds but also are "characters." They are large enough and noisy enough to be conspicuous and they intrigue us with their activities. The crows are generally considered to be the most intelligent of birds and can learn to count up to five or six. That their capacity to learn a few words such as "Hello" or "Pretty Boy" is a sign of intelligence is debatable. Their intelligence is perhaps best shown in the ability of the crow to adapt to changed conditions, to profit by man's agricultural practices, and to survive the persecution of farmers, of bird-lovers who deplore their robbing of songbirds' nests, or of sportsman's intolerance of their depredations on ducks' eggs and young.

The crow family is nearly world-wide and has 15 species in North America north of Mexico. In size the birds are from 10 to 25 inches long; in color they are black, boldly black and white, or with blue, gray or green predominating. The sexes are alike. Some, like the crows and the magpies, walk on the ground to feed but fly to trees to perch. The jays are more tree birds. All are robust with a stout pointed bill and they eat a wide variety of food, animal and vegetable, depending on availability. A bulky nest, domed in the case of the magpie, is built in a tree and three to ten or more greenish, spotted eggs are laid. In winter some northern populations migrate southward. The species are here considered under the following headings: crows and ravens, magpies, crowjays and jays.

CROWS AND RAVENS

Everyone knows the common crow (*Corvus brachyrhynchos*). It is the 21-inch black bird that sits in the top of a tree and utters a noisy "caw caw caw." It also walks about in newly mown hayfields to catch grasshoppers and in harvested grain fields for waste grain. It will eat garbage and along the coast it scavenges for edible items washed up by the sea. Shellfish are broken open by being carried up into the air and dropped on a rock. There is little, vegetable or animal, that the crow does not eat.

The crow's needs seem to be met best by farming country of culti ed fields and pastures, scattered woodlots and tree-lined fence rows. Often living near man and with a remarkable sense of self-preservation, it is probably more abundant now than it was under primitive conditions. Its range covers almost the whole United States. Northern populations move southward at the approach of cold weather, and winter crow roosts in central states like Oklahoma may contain many thousands of birds. In parts of southern Canada in the spring the call of the crow is the first spring bird voice.

The related fish crow (*Corvus ossifragus*) of the eastern seaboard and the northwestern crow (*Corvus caurinus*) of the Pacific northwestern coast area are very similar to the common crow but are slightly smaller, have hoarse or more nasal calls, and their favorite feeding grounds are the shores and mudflats along the sea. Sometimes, however, they feed inland. Compared with the common crow the common raven (*Corvus corax*) is a bigger, heavier bird with longer wings and wedge-shaped tail. Instead of the crow's "caw" the raven has a loud, hoarse "croa-a-ak" as the most

Top: Common raven (Corvus corax)   181
Bottom: Clark's nutcracker (Nucifraga columbiana)

distinctive item in its extensive vocabulary. It is also a more northern bird and prefers wilderness areas, the Arctic coast and barrens and the coniferous forests of the North and the mountains. The white-necked raven (*Corvus cryptoleucus*) of farmland in the Southwest is very like the common crow but with more of a wedgeshaped tail and the voice of a raven. The white bases of the feathers of the hind neck are usually concealed.

MAGPIES

The black-billed magpie (*Pica pica*) is a conspicuous black and white bird of the West with a tail accounting for more than half of its 18-inch length. It needs open country in which to walk when seeking grasshoppers and beetles in season and grain as an emergency ration in the lean times of winter and it needs trees or shrubs in which to roost and nest. These it finds from the western edge of the plains to the Pacific and north to Alaska. It also favors flesh, following coyotes, and hoping for scraps from their kill; it used to wait about Indian camps for anything edible and trailed behind buffalo hunters for refuse from the hunt. With the coming of settlement the magpie proved a bold, inquisitive but suspicious bird quick to take alarm, enabling it to coexist with settlers, using their fields and even finding refuge from the severity of winter nights by roosting on the backs of cattle in open sheds. Although the enmity of ranchers has been aroused by belief that the magpies pick at open sores, cuts and branding iron scars on the backs of stock, magpies have been kept as pets since Indian days and extravagant claims have been made for the size of the vocabularies of certain individuals. Its ordinary call is sometimes written "cack cack" but it also has a wide variety of notes, some harsh, some musical, as I found when awakened one morning by a party of magpies "talking" on the sheet iron roof of the "house" in which I was staying.

The yellow-billed magpie (*Pica nuttalli*), found in farming country of the central valleys of California, differs chiefly from the black-billed magpie by its yellow bill.

CROW-JAYS

The pinyon jay and the Clark's nutcracker (*Nucifraga columbiana*) share the appearance and habits of both crows and jays. The pinyon jay (*Gymnorhinus cyanocephala*) might better have been called the little blue crow in reference to its small size (11 inches long), its jaylike blue color,

Blue jay (Cyanocitta cristata)

its crowlike form with a short tail and long bill, and its crowlike habits of walking when on the ground and of feeding and flying in compact flocks. Its name, pinyon jay, refers to the bird's dependence on the pinyon pine, the major tree in its favorite habitat—the pinyon-juniper belt of the western mountains—which supplies its favorite food, the seeds from the cones on the trees from the ground after the seeds have been shed. In winter, flocks may wander widely in other habitats and eat a variety of foods.

The Clark's nutcracker (*Nucifraga columbiana*), with a rather short tail and long bill, is about 13 inches long and gray with black and white wings. It is a boisterous, noisy, inquisitive species, feeding on a wide variety of food in a variety of ways. It extracts seeds from cones in the treetops, digs grubs from the bark, catches insects on the wing and visits campsites for scraps in its summer home at high altitudes among the conifers of the western mountains.

JAYS

The blue and white, crested blue jay (*Cyanocitta cristata*) of the northeastern woodlands is well known as a noisy, boisterous bird going in small parties in the autumn, hopping through the branches, scolding an owl or squirrel here, hacking open a beechnut there. Suddenly, for no apparent reason, a whole party may break into frantic screams, crests raised and tails fanned. Apparently these jays get more rude fun out of life than do most birds. Later many move south but some linger to eke out an existence with stored nuts and suet at feeding stations. In the South the blue jay is a sedentary, quiet bird and lives not only in wood and orchard but in gardens and shade trees of villages and towns. The Steller's jay (*Cyanocitta stelleri*) replaces the blue jay in the coniferous forests of the Rocky Mountains and the Pacific coast area. It has the form and many of the habits of the blue jay, but the color pattern is quite different. The long crest, head and forepart of the body is dark sooty and there is no conspicuous white in the rest of its blue plumage.

The main range of scrub jays (*Aphelocoma coerulescens*) is in the oak-scrubs of the West and the Southwest, with an isolated population in Florida. This jay has a gentler, quieter, more retiring disposition than that of the blue jays and spends much of its time hidden in the dense thickets. Yet unlike the blue jay it often flies to the topmost branches of an oak or

Steller's jay (Cyanocitta stelleri)

hickory and sits quietly upright, tail pointed straight down. It also is easily tamed to take food from a person's hand and then perch on his arm or head. In shape and deportment these crestless jays recall not the blue jays but the gray jays of the boreal forests despite the difference in color— blue and drab upperparts, whitish underparts with a dark band across the upper breast. In the oak and pines of the higher mountains of the Southwest lives the related Mexican jay *(Aphelocoma ultramarina)* which is duller and lacks the dark band across the breast. A still more different crestless jay from Mexico is the green jay *(Cyanocorax yncas)* that reaches southeastern Texas. It is bright green except for the blue and black head and throat.

The gray jay *(Perisoreus canadensis)* is a boreal bird of the spruce forests of the Far North and the western mountains. In late summer the traveler through the stunted spruce country is likely to be joined by a family party of these birds. As silent as ghosts they come, flapping and gliding, and the long broad tail and wide rounded wings give them a striking silhouette. Each perches quietly on a spruce top, the sooty black young and the adults clad in various shades of gray with white forehead and a black nape, all

185

with a blank innocent expression. Another aspect of their character was revealed one noon in camp when bread from the plates and bacon from the frying pan was carried off quietly from an unguarded lunch. Strangely, they nest early when snow is deep on the ground and temperatures fall to zero.

Chickadees, Titmice, Verdin and Bushtits (*Family Paridae*)

Chickadees are favorites at bird feeders, for many spend the winter in the North, come freely to eat suet and nut meats and are tame, spritely little birds that seem cheery and friendly. One of my earliest memories of a bird is of a chickadee that perched on my hand to eat the suet half hidden by my fingers. The natural winter food is dormant insects and spider eggs gleaned from twig and bark. In summer of course a greater variety of insects are available. The birds are active, acrobatic mites always on the move, flitting here and there, perching right side up or swinging upside down or clinging to an upright twig. Often in winter the chickadees go in little parties to which other small insect-eaters such as kinglets, nuthatches, a brown creeper and a small woodpecker may attach themselves.

The nest is placed in a hole in a tree and up to ten white, lightly dotted eggs are laid. Besides the chickadees the family includes the tufted titmouse, the verdin and the bushtits, and there are many Old World species as well as the fourteen species in America.

CHICKADEES

There are seven chickadee species, all very similar in pattern, in America. The black-capped chickadee (*Parus atricapillus*) is the most widespread in the woodlands across the continent and is 5 inches long, gray and white with black cap and bib and white face. It tends to prefer hardwood forest and woodlots. Besides its familiar "chick-a-dee" it has a two-note, whistled spring song. In the Southeast is the very similar Carolina chickadee (*Parus carolinensis*); in the mountain pine forests along the Mexican border lives the darker Mexican chickadee (*Parus sclateri*); and

186

in the coniferous forests of the West lives the mountain chickadee (*Parus gambeli*), the only chickadee with a black line through the eye.

The boreal chickadee (*Parus hudsonicus*) is a bird of the northern coniferous forests and has the back and cap brown; the paler gray-headed chickadee (*Parus cinctus*) lives in the Far Northwest on the edge of the Arctic tundra; and the chestnut-backed chickadee (*Parus rufescens*) of the Pacific coast area has a black cap and chestnut back and flanks.

TITMICE

In the Midwest, the loud, whistled "Pet-er- Pet-er Pet-er" of the tufted titmouse (*Parus bicolor*) shares with the song of the cardinal the beginning of the season of spring bird songs before the earliest migrants have arrived and while it is yet winter, although the days are lengthening. All winter the titmice had come to our feeding station where they preferred sunflower seeds, holding them in their feet and hacking them open. Although very chickadee-like, the titmouse is slightly larger, slower and less agile. Like the chickadee it makes the nest in a hole in a tree.

The tufted titmouse of the woodlots and forests of the eastern half of the country is 6 inches long, gray above, whitish below with white face and chestnut flanks. The related black-crested titmouse (*Parus atricristatus*) with a black crest replaces the tufted titmouse in southeastern Texas. In the Southwest there is the plain titmouse (*Parus inornatus*), like the tufted titmouse, but much paler, while in the mountains of southern Arizona and New Mexico lives the bridled titmouse (*Parus wollweberi*) with two black lines across its face.

VERDIN

The tiny 4-inch-long verdin (*Auriparus flaviceps*) is the representative of the chickadees in the deserts of the Southwest where it flits and hops amongst the harsh, thorny shrubbery and cactus, as acrobatic as a chickadee, looking for insects and sometimes eating berries. Quite unlike a chickadee in color, however, the plumage is gray above white below with much of the head and throat yellow in the male. Both sexes have chestnut shoulders. The verdin's nest is remarkable; it is an oval ball of twigs with a side entrance and is placed among the twigs of a desert shrub. The birds are permanent residents going about in small parties in the winter when they sleep in nests they have built.

187

BUSHTITS

A loose flock of six to twenty or more tiny gray birds drifting through the oaks and shrubbery along a roadside in the West and the Far West are likely to be common bushtits *(Psaltriparus minimus).* Their actions are like those of chickadees though their tails are rather long and the 4-inch-long birds have none of the conspicuous markings usual in the chickadee family. Like its relative the verdin, the bushtit's outstanding feature is its nest. Unlike the verdin's nest, however, the bushtit's is not thorny but is saclike, sometimes as long as 7 to 10 inches, and hangs from a branch the young are raised they keep together, foraging over bark, branch and into this is caught bits of plant material that help disguise the nest. Once the young are raised they keep together, foraging over bark, branch and twig for insects, and family group joins family group to make up their characteristic winter aggregations.

A second species, the black-eared bushtit *(Psaltriparus melanotis)* is similar but may be recognized by the black patch on the side of the head in the male. It lives in the desert mountains near where New Mexico and Texas join Old Mexico and also southward.

Nuthatches *(Family Sittidae)*

The nuthatches are birds of tree trunks and branches where they hop in any direction, up, down or across. Indeed, they seem to prefer a head-down position at times, as when one of them puts a piece of suet or a sunflower seed behind the upper edge of a flake of bark and hammers it to pieces from above. The white-breasted nuthatch at our winter feeding station prefers sunflower seeds to suet while the reverse is true of the red-breasted nuthatch. The natural food of the nuthatches includes not only many insects and spiders from the bark of trees, but also nuts and the seeds of spruces and pines. As one might expect of a tree trunk bird, the nest is made in either a natural cavity or a hole excavated by the bird. The five to nine eggs are white, sparsely dotted with brown.

The four species of nuthatches are from 4 to 6 inches long with short tails, rather long wings and straight bills. The back is gray, the crown gray, black or brown and the underparts are white or buffy to rufous

White-breasted nuthatch (Sitta carolinensis)

tinged. The largest and most widely distributed species is the white-breasted nuthatch (*Sitta carolinensis*) with the crown black and the whole face and underparts white. It is a permanent resident, especially of deciduous woodland, across the United States and commonly comes to shade trees of towns and gardens. Its usual call is a nasal "yank" and its spring-time song is a series of whistled notes. The smaller red-breasted nuthatch (*Sitta canadensis*) has a black crown, black line through the eye and buffy rufous underparts. It summers in the coniferous forest of the North and West and winters southward. In the southeast woodland country lives the brown-headed nuthatch (*Sitta pusilla*) and in the West is the pigmy nuthatch (*Sitta pygmaea*) with a gray crown like the back.

Brown Creeper (*Family Certhiidae*)

The brown creeper (*Certhia familiaris*) is a small, unobtrusive bird whose day is one of quiet routine, of hitching or "creeping" a spiral course up one tree trunk and dropping as softly as a blown leaf to the base of the next tree to continue the search for its food of small insects. The creeper is about 5 inches long, brownish streaked with whitish above, to harmonize with the bark, and white below with a fine, curved bill, sharp claws and a relatively long, pointed tail whose feathers serve as a brace in climbing. The brown creeper is the only species in America of an otherwise entirely Old World family.

The coniferous forests of the northern and western part of the continent are the summer home of the brown creeper; there it wedges its nest under a loose flake of bark and lays five to nine white, sparsely spotted eggs. In winter the more northern birds move southward. The birds sometimes join little bands of roving chickadees and kinglets.

Wrentit (*Family Chamaeidae*)

The wrentit family, the only bird family peculiar to North America, has but a single species restricted to the Pacific coast area. The wrentit (*Chamaea fasciata*) is a tiny wren-like bird about 6 inches long, half of which is tail. In color it is plain brown with a pale line over the eye, pale streaking on its breast and a pale yellow eye.

The wrentit is not only a permanent resident but it forms a permanent pair. Each is a lifelong resident of the acre or so of the dense brush called chaparral that it holds as its territory. Here the birds forage out of sight among the twigs for insects and berries. The ringing song, heard more often than the bird is seen, is a series of whistle-like notes. The cup-shaped nest in a bush is finished in cobweb and the three to five eggs are pale blue green.

Dippers (*Family Cinclidae*)

The clear dashing streams with cascades, riffles and quiet, foam-flecked pools of the western mountains are the haunts of the dipper (*Cinclus mexicanus*), a song bird that has taken to an aquatic life. Like a large wren in appearance but with a dense waterproof coat of feathers, the dipper flies along the streams, perches on spray-drenched rocks where it bobs up and down, wades in riffles and disappears underwater to search for its food of insects, other invertebrates and tiny fish. How it gets about underwater is still discussed: does it swim with its wings or with its feet (which are not webbed) or walk on the bottom held down by the pressure of the current on its back? Probably all three methods are used.

Early in the year the male sings an elaborate song, often muffled by the sound of the rushing water. In the spring the large, domed nest is built, usually on a rocky ledge within reach of the spray from a stream, and there three to six white eggs are laid.

We have but one species of dipper, about 6 inches long, wrenlike and short-tailed. Male, female and young are the same dull gray. The family is a small one with other species in South America and Eurasia.

Wrens (*Family Troglodytidae*)

Wrens are small brown birds that are bundles of nervous energy, shy, quick and always on the move, adept at creeping unseen through tangles of shrubbery, grass or jumbles of rock, bold to the point of impudence as they pop in and out of cover, tail cocked over back, scolding an intruder. They are contradictory little birds. Some have been likened to mice or chipmunks as they hop and flit under cover, yet they may mount to conspicuous perches to give loud songs of pleasing musical quality. Some make nests in holes in trees and crannies among rocks and buildings; others make domed nests in the cactus or grass in which they live. The eggs are numerous, up to eight or ten in a clutch, and are white or brownish with or without dark spots.

The wren family is American, with one species in Eurasia. In the United States there are ten species, mostly small, 3 ½ to 7 ½ inches long, and brown predominates in their plumage with black barring or streaking. The sexes are alike. The tail is short to moderate in length and the bill is slender for picking up insects and spiders that are their chief food. Some species occur in almost every part of the United States and northern birds migrate south for the winter.

There are three wrens that are intimately associated with man's dwellings and gardens in one or another part of their ranges: the house wren (*Troglodytes aedon*), 4 ½ inches long, pale brownish below and summering across the northern two-thirds of the country; the Bewick's wren (*Thryomanes bewickii*) differing in having white underparts and eyebrow stripe and living in the southern two-thirds of the continent; and the larger Carolina wren (*Thryothorus ludovicianus*) of the Southeast, 5 inches long, with white eyebrow and throat and the rest of the underparts buffy.

The house wren has two poses, one, sitting on a twig, tail down, head up while he gives his bubbling song, and the other, head down and tail cocked up as he hops from branch to branch in the shrubbery, harshly scolding some prowling cat. Probably more common in towns and villages than in the country, he is a tenant of many a bird house. But any hole or cavity in a tree, wall, old tin can, cow skull or pocket of a discarded coat will do. One amusing spring sight is to see a wren with a crooked twig, larger than he is, billing it through a hole no larger than his body. Once the nest is made the wren is not satisifed and may go on and fill other holes in his territory. Perhaps from aggressiveness, perhaps from pure cussedness, he may puncture the eggs of other birds in the vicinity.

Where the house wren is absent, the Bewick's takes its place as the "house wren," equally familiar, choosing the same variety of odd nest sites and creeping and hopping, now appearing, now disappearing in the shrubbery of garden or dry hillside. In character, however, there is a difference. The Bewick's seems a more gentle, more deliberate bird and its varied song is clearer and sweeter, delivered from a roadside bush or the roof of a house. I have seen a pair of Carolina wrens in a backyard apple tree near Chicago but I always think of it as belonging to the Deep South, where its familiar habits give it the local name of "house" wren, and to Florida where it lives everywhere— in oak and cabbage hammocks, in swamps and in damp thickets— and is one of our great songsters.

There are two other wrens very similar to the house wren: the brown-throated wren (*Troglodytes brunneicollis*), with a more buffy throat, of Mexico and the mountains of southern Arizona, and the winter wren (*Troglodytes troglodytes*), smaller, darker and shorter tailed, that summers in the wilderness of coniferous forests of the North and in the mountains.

There are three desert and rock wrens of the Southwest and West. The cactus wren (*Campylorhynchus brunneicapillus*), 7 ½ inches long, is our largest wren. It is conspicuous in the cactus and thorny bush of the deserts and has a heavily patterned plumage, including a white, spotted breast, a variety of harsh grating calls, squawks and buzzes as well as a pleasing song, and a flask-shaped nest often seen among the spiny joints of the cholla cactus. The rock wren (*Salpinctes obsoletus*) lives among the jumbles of broken rock and earthen erosion gulches of open plains and slopes. It builds its nest under a rock and paves the entrance with pebbles. The bird is generally brown above, white below with fine breast streaks. The canyon wren (*Catherpes mexicanus*) has a white throat contrasting with a rufous belly and prefers to live among the rocky walls of canyons.

There are two marsh wrens, both of which make oval nests with side entrances placed among marsh vegetation. The longbilled marsh wren (*Telmatodytes palustris*), 5 inches long, has a white streaked back, a solid rufous crown, and lives in stands of cattails, rushes and grasses growing in shallow water. When the male sings he may throw back his head and cock up his tail until they almost meet. The smaller short-billed marsh wren (*Cistothorus platensis*) is a shy elusive bird of dryer marshes and wet meadows.

Mockingbirds, Catbird and Thrashers (*Family Mimidae*)

Outstanding songs characterize all of the mockingbird family although this capacity for song is best developed in the mockingbird (*Mimus polyglottos*) itself. It is a strongly territorial as well as pugnacious bird. This aggressiveness is directed not only against its own kind, but other bird species, in and out of the nesting season. For example, one October in south Florida a mockingbird had included a fruit-laden Brazilian pepper berry tree in its territory. Numerous migrant catbirds (*Dumetella carolinensis*), newly arrived from the North, persisted in visiting the tree for the berries. This kept the defending mockingbird so busy that periodically he became exhausted, flew to a nearby dripping faucet for a drink and then rested a while on a shady perch before returning to chase the catbirds.

Several species of the family, however, are tolerant of the proximity of man. Mockingbirds, catbirds and brown thrashers (*Toxostoma rufum*) nest in garden shrubbery in parts of the East, while the same mockingbird and the California thrasher (*Toxostoma redivivum*) frequent dooryards in the California area and the curve-billed thrasher (*Toxostoma curvirostre*) and the Bendire's thrasher (*Toxostoma bendirei*) come about towns or the vicinity of farm buildings in Arizona.

The mockingbird family is entirely of the New World with ten species in the United States. They are songbirds, 8 to 13 inches long, with short wings, long tail, and a short straight or a long curved bill. Their predominant coloration is gray, slaty or plain brown. Three thrashers have heavily streaked breasts. The favorite habitat of these birds is open brushy country. There they can hop or run on the ground in the open, get much of their insect food, and fly to shrubbery for shelter and feed on fruits and berries. Their rich musical songs are usually uttered from some conspicuous perch. The basin-shaped nest is placed in some shrub or low tree and the three to six eggs are some shade of blue, green or grayish with or without spots.

The species are arranged here in the following sequence: mockingbird, catbird, brown thrashers, curve-billed and other desert and sage thrashers.

MOCKINGBIRD

From the citrus groves of California to the gardens of the low country of the Carolinas, the mockingbird (*Mimus polyglottos*) finds suburban and village lawns with shrubs and trees more attractive than its natural habitat of native shrubs, grasses and cactus. From some conspicuous perch they pour out their famous song: loud, rollicking and long continued and, by tradition, associated with the Deep South, magnolias and moonlight. Characteristically, notes are repeated three or more times and in addition to the melodious phrases there may be harsher notes. Some gifted individuals also utilize many imitations of such diverse sounds as notes of other birds, the bark of a dog, the noise of a frog, or the sounds of farm machinery.

The mockingbird is a permanent resident that may sing and hold territory much of the year. When at rest the mockingbird appears mostly gray and white, but in flight the black and white of wings and tail flash conspicuously.

Top: Cactus wren (*Campylorhynchus brunneicapillus*)   195
Bottom: Brown thrasher (*Toxostoma rufum*)

CATBIRD

Plain slaty gray with a black cap and rusty undertail coverts, the catbird (*Dumetella carolinensis*), 8½ inches long, is more modest and retiring than the mockingbird and spends more time in the shrubbery. But it is also a familiar bird of lawns and garden shrubbery and has an outstanding song, delivered from a conspicuous or a concealed perch and distinguished from that of the mockingbird by each note being uttered only once. Imitations of other birds are sometimes used, but the "mew" that gives the bird its name is the catbird's protest note, not an imitation of a cat. The species ranges over the eastern and central part of the country and winters south of our border, except in Florida where it lives mostly on berries.

BROWN THRASHERS

The brown thrasher (*Toxostoma rufum*) is 11-12 inches long and has a foxy brown back and a streaked breast. In the northeastern states it is a bird of forest edge and brushy pastures on dry hillsides and is shyer and less familiar than the catbird. In the Midwest, however, it comes into the shrubbery of gardens and may even nest near houses.

The song is distinguishable from that of its eastern near relatives by the notes being repeated twice, not sung just once as with the catbird, nor three or more times as with the mockingbird. Like these near relatives the brown thrasher forages for insects on the ground but unlike them it throws leaves aside in its foraging and also digs into the ground with its bill. In the autumn the brown thrasher eats not only berries and fruit but also nuts and corn.

The similar, closely related long-billed thrasher (*Toxostoma longirostre*) is a Mexican species that crosses the Rio Grande only in southern Texas.

CURVE-BILLED THRASHER AND RELATIVES

The curve-billed thrasher (*Toxostoma curvirostre*) is one of the five earthy or earth-brown desert thrashers and has the widest range—from Arizona to southern Texas. It is one of the common and conspicuous birds of the desert flats and mesas. There it runs and hops over the sun-baked earth, digs into the soil and sweeps away surface litter in its search for insects, flies to scattered shrubs and cactus to perch and sing its clear, melodious phrases, with little repetition. The cholla cactus with its loose-jointed branches, thickly armed with needle-like spines, seems formidable

Eastern bluebird (Sialia sialis)

to a tenderfoot. But it seems to present no problem to this thrasher who perches, makes its nest and sleeps in it. The curve-bill seems to form permanent pairs and though a permanent resident, may forsake the mesas in winter for the shrubbery of the more sheltered valleys.

Four other related thrashers, all with loud, pleasing songs, occur in the deserts and brushlands of the arid and semi-arid Southwest: the Bendire's thrasher (*Toxostoma bendirei*), the California thrasher (*Toxostoma redivivum*), the crissal thrasher (*Toxostoma dorsale*), and the Le Conte's thrasher (*Toxostoma lecontei*).

Rather different in appearance is the sage thrasher (*Oreoscoptes montanus*) which summers in the great sagebrush plains of the West and winters south into Mexico. It is a small bird, only 8-9 inches long, with a short straight bill, a heavily streaked breast and a white-tipped tail and is the only one of the family that commonly sings its beautiful song while flying in great circles over the sage.

Thrushes (*Family Turdidae*)

In early January of each year the local newspapers of the Northeast are likely to carry a report of the arrival of the first spring robins, despite the fact that a few robins normally stay the winter and the real migrants will not come for another month or two. But this illustrates how well known and well liked the robin is. Equally well liked but less well known are the bluebirds, while the notable songs of the related spot-breasted song thrushes of the woodlands are favorites of those who visit wilderness areas.

The thrush family occurs in both the Old and the New World and there are 13 species in the United States and Canada. They are small to medium-sized song birds, 6-10 inches long, that live in woodlands or semi-wooded areas. Their diet is mixed, including insects and earthworms obtained on the ground and fruits from trees. Their cup-shaped nests are placed in trees, a cavity in a tree trunk, or in a bank, and the three to six eggs are blue or white, with or without spots. Migration is the rule, though some, such as the robin and bluebird, retire only slightly from the northern parts of the range, while others such as the Swainson's thrush migrate from their northern breeding grounds to winter in South America.

The arrangement here of the 13 species is as follows: robin and varied thrush; spot-breasted song thrushes; bluebirds; solitaire and other thrushes.

ROBIN

One of the best-known and favorite birds is the red-breasted robin (*Turdus migratorius*) that hops or runs over lawns pulling up worms, skirmishes with its neighbors over its territory, builds its cup-shaped, mud-reinforced nests in the large fork of a shade tree or on the ledge of a house, and starts its cheery song of warbled phrases from a treetop at first light. True, the robin may gorge on sweet cherries, its nest may clog a rain spout and its habit of persistently shadow-boxing its reflection in a picture window may be annoying, but we still look forward to its return in the early spring.

Where the robin summers in wilderness country of open tree stands, from New England to Alaska, its temperament is different. There it is a wild, shy bird. In winter a few stay in the North but most gather in great flocks that move over the countryside of our southeastern states, looking for crops of small fruits such as palmetto fruit, china tree berries and beach plums.

The robin is about 10 inches long and has a red breast, dark gray back and a darker crown; the young have the breast spotted. In the western forests lives the related varied thrush (*Ixoreus naevius*) with an orange-rufous breast crossed by a black band.

SPOT-BREASTED SONG THRUSHES

It takes a keen eye to identify all the five thrushes of this group: wood thrush, hermit thrush, Swainson's thrush, gray-cheeked thrush and veery. All are about the same size, 7 to 8 inches long, and all are brown above and white below with the breast spotted. These birds are trim, quiet, deliberate, big-eyed birds of the forest shade. They fly and perch freely but feed much on the ground; a few hops, a pause, and a worm is picked up or a leaf tossed aside so the bird can scan the soil for uncovered invertebrates. Yet, as with many insect eaters, when berries are ripe these thrushes feed on them as they do in their wintering grounds from the southern United States to South America. On spring migration the birds are silent; their songs are reserved for their breeding grounds in the northern and western forests and the woodlands of the East.

The wood thrush (*Hylocichla mustelina*) with a rufous head and olive brown back summers in the shady, damp woodlands of the East. Its song is a series of spaced phrases, variable in pitch and with a rich bell-like quality. The hermit thrush (*Hylocichla guttata*) of the mixed forests of the North and West has a brown back and a russet tail and its song differs from that of the wood thrush in being clearer, more musical and silvery, rather rich and bell-like. The veery (*Hylocichla fuscescens*), with whole upperparts russet (or olive brown in the West) and faint breast spotting, breeds from New England to the western mountains and its song is a downward rolling or slurring series of silvery notes. The gray-cheeked thrush (*Hylocichla minima*) of the far northern forests is olive brown above with a gray face and its song is somewhat veery-like but with an ascending slurring. The Swainson's thrush (*Hylocichla ustulata*) of the northern forests, with olive brown back and buffy face and eye-ring, has a simpler song than the wood thrush that tends to slur upward.

BLUEBIRDS

The eastern bluebird (*Sialia sialis*) is a gentle, friendly bird of the semi-open country. Farmlands with old orchards, shade trees, woodlots and open fields are favored. The bluebird sits up quietly on post, twig or wire and flies out to snap up an insect in the air, a caterpillar from a leaf or a beetle or grasshopper from the ground. The nest is in a natural tree cavity or an old woodpecker hole and the bird takes readily to bird boxes. The more northern birds move south for the winter but they return early in the spring, and inclement weather then may decimate populations, a catastrophe from which it may take years to recover. This, and the competition of the more aggressive house sparrow and starling for nest sites, may have contributed to a decrease in bluebird populations.

The male of the eastern bluebird of the eastern part of the country is blue above with an earthy red breast and white belly. There are two other bluebirds: the western bluebird (*Sialia mexicana*) of western United States is like the eastern bluebird but with blue on the throat and a red-brown patch on the back, while the mountain bluebird (*Sialia currucoides*) of western Canada and the United States is generally blue with a white belly.

TOWNSEND'S SOLITAIRE

A thrush trying to sing like a winter wren was my thought as I heard my first Townsend's solitaire (*Myadestes townsendi*) singing in the open stand

Top: *Wood thrush* (*Hylocichla mustelina*)
Bottom: *Curve-billed thrasher* (*Toxostoma curvirostre*)

of conifers near timberline in the Yukon mountains. I later found it a seven-inch long, slim, gray bird showing pale patches in its wings and white in its tail as it flew. Often it sat up quietly, hawking insects like a fly-catcher and occasionally flyng down like a bluebird to pounce on some small prey, worm or insect, on the ground. Its nest is placed in a hollow in a cut bank or under a log or stone; the eggs are whitish, spotted brown. Summering in the western mountains, the solitaire moves downward or southward in winter in parties and flocks and changes to a diet of berries.

OTHER THRUSHES

Two small species of Old World thrushes are of limited occurrence in the Arctic: the wheatear (*Oenanthe ocenanthe*), a black and white bird, and the bluethroat (*Luscinia svecica*) a brownish bird with blue in the throat and a reddish base to the tail.

Kinglets, Gnatcatchers and Old World Warblers (*Family Sylviidae*)

Kinglets are such tiny birds that individuals have been found caught on winter burdock heads. Nearly as small as hummingbirds, kinglets are olive-green and olive-gray fluffy birds, 3¼-4 inches long, that have a peculiar habit of flicking their wing tips, adding to the appearance of nervous activity as the birds continually flit and hop among twigs and leaves in search of their food of tiny insects, their eggs and larvae.

The summer home of both kinglets is in the spruce forests of the North and of the mountains. Here a deep, thick cup-shaped nest of moss, fur and feathers is nestled among spruce twigs so that it is semi-pensile and well camouflaged. The eggs, white with a few small spots, are remarkably numerous, often 8 or 9 in number, a clutch size equalling that of some chick-adees. After the nesting season many of the birds move south even as far as Florida and California for the winter. Then they frequent many sorts of woodlands, brush and garden shrubs and often seem singulary indifferent to a human's presence.

Both kinglets have two wing bars. The ruby-crowned kinglet (*Regulus calendula*) has also a white eye-ring that gives the face a curiously blank expression and the male has a ruby red crown spot which is flashed conspicuously in times of excitement. Its song is a rich "liberty liberty liberty," amazingly loud for the size of the bird. The golden-crowned kinglet (*Regulus satrapa*) has a yellow or orange crown edged with black, a white line above the eye and a black line through it. The song is a series of high, lisping notes. In winter the golden-crowned often joins foraging bands of chickadees.

The blue-gray gnatcatcher (*Polioptila caerulea*) would be no longer than a kinglet if it were not for a long tail that gives it an extra inch or so in length, and a slender appearance to which its coloration, blue-gray above, white below, adds an elegant daintiness. The tail is often cocked up over the back and switched about in a manner that has given rise to comparisons with the much larger mockingbird and catbird. However, the gnatcatcher likes to live among the branches of the deciduous woodlands of the East and the oak associations of the West, where it is a nervously active bird continually flying or hopping from branch to twig snapping up tiny insects in the air or hovering by leaf or twig to snatch off a crawling insect.

The nest is a small neat cup of soft plant material bound together with cobweb, decorated with lichen, and saddled on a branch. The four to five eggs are whitish, spotted brown. Northern birds are migratory, but southern ones are permanent residents.

The related black-tailed gnatcatcher (*Polioptila melanura*) is a permanent resident of the Southwest in the desert trees and shrubbery. The fifth member of this predominantly Old World family in America is the arctic warbler (*Phylloscopus borealis*) that has extended its range from Siberia to southern Asia for the winter. The arctic warbler is 5 inches long, olive above, whitish below and with a pale stripe over the eye. It makes a domed nest on the ground.

Pipits and Wagtails *(Family Motacillidae)*

There is only one pipit most Americans are likely to see—the water pipit (*Anthus spinoletta*). In migration or in winter it occurs over much of the

United States in open country such as plowed fields, short grass areas, salt marshes and beaches. There it walks about seeking its food of insects and seeds. This pipit often goes in loose flocks and the birds' backs harmonize so well with the ground that the first intimation one may have of their presence is the birds flying up, showing their white outer tail feathers as they go.

The Arctic barrens and the alpine tundra of western mountain tops are the summer home of the water pipit, where it walks about on the ground foraging for insects. The song is given on the wing while the male flies upward as much as fifty yards, then with fluttering wings floats back to earth. The nest is placed on the ground and the four to seven eggs are white with extensive brown markings. With the close of the short Arctic summer the pipits move south to winter in the southern states and south to Central America.

The water pipit, 7 inches long, is rather sparrow-like in its gray-brown, lightly streaked underparts. The bill is slender, the outer tail feathers are white, and as the bird walks it often wags its tail.

The related but more heavily streaked Sprague's pipit (*Anthus spragueii*) is a summer bird of the northern prairies. As autumn approaches the birds gather into flocks and move south in a narrow migration route to winter in Mexico.

Wagtails differ from pipits in being boldly patterned, with longer tails and, logically, more exaggerated tail wagging. Two species occur in America, summering only in far northwestern Alaska and returning to Asia for the winter: the white wagtail (*Motacilla alba*), and the yellow wagtail (*Motacilla flava*). This family, Motacillidae, with four species in America, has a large and more diversified representation in the Old World.

Waxwings *(Family Bombycillidae)*

There are only two species in the waxwing family; both occur in North America and one also ranges in Eurasia. Sometime during the cold weather a flock of cedar waxwings (*Bombycilla cedrorum*) arrives in the village where I live near Chicago, and one by one the high bush cranberries and rowan trees are denuded of their bright red berries. During most of the year the waxwings perch, feed and fly in flocks of a dozen or a score of

Top: Water pipit (Anthus spinoletta)
Bottom: Cedar waxwing (Bombycilla cedrorum)

birds. A flock may swirl away, fly high, and alight again high in a tree. They often line up sociably on a branch or telephone wire, and there is no quarreling. Indeed, the birds may pass a berry from bill to bill down a whole line of birds and even back again. This berry passing seems to be a leisure activity or play and may be an extension of the berry passing used in courtship when one of a pair may ape the begging-for-food behavior of the young. Although a weak warbling song has been reported, voice seems little used in courtship and the lisping hiss often given as the bird flies is not notable.

The nest is usually placed well out on the branch of a tree, usually at some height, and the eggs, three to five in number, are bluish-gray with a few spots. The cedar waxwing is a late nester, and feeds berries and fruits to the nestlings, a rather unusual food for nestling song birds.

The cedar waxwing, about 7 inches long, is pale brown and with a crest. It summers in the northern states and southern Canada and northern birds move southward in winter. The related Bohemian waxwing (*Bombycilla garrula*) is a more northern bird of the Northwest which wanders irregularly as far east as the Great Lakes.

Silky Flycatchers (*Family Ptilogonatidae*)

The phainopepla (*Phainopepla nitens*) is a conspicuous bird of the shrubbery and trees of the southwestern deserts and resembles no other North American bird. About 8 inches long, slender, long-tailed and crested, the male appears all black as he sits in the top of a mesquite. When he makes display flights over his territory, the concealed white wing patches are conspicuous. Occasionally he flies to a distant grove of cotton-woods to feed on abundant mistletoe berries. He has already built the frame of a nest when a gray, crested female joins him. There is a passing of berries in courtship feeding, mutual courtship flights, and then the female lines the nest, a small, shallow cup saddled into a fork, and lays two white, brown-spotted eggs in it. Both sexes incubate and when the young hatch both parents bring berries in their gullets and regurgitate them for the young. After fledging, the birds gather into flocks and wander southward, leaving parts of their range vacant.

The silky flycatcher family is found only in the Panama—southwestern United States area with four species, only one of which, the phainopepla, reaches the southwestern United States.

Shrikes *(Family Laniidae)*

A driver in the open country of Florida or California will find the logger-head strike *(Lanius ludovicianus)* one of the conspicuous roadside birds. Its colors, gray, white and black, are those of a mockingbird, but in flight the big head, rapidly beating wings, and long, thin tail is distinctive; so is its habit of sitting quietly on a telephone wire or the topmost twig of a tree or bush.

Shrikes are song birds with some of the habits of birds of prey. They catch large insects, small lizards, mice and small birds, kill them by biting with their heavy, hooked bills, and then impale them on thorns or barbs of fence wire where they can be pulled to pieces. Open country with scattered shrubs for perches and nests is the shrike's favorite habitat. The song is a series of trills, clear notes and harsher ones. The bulky nest of sticks is placed in a dense shrub and four to six grayish, brown-spotted eggs are laid.

Shrikes are chiefly an Old World family, with only two species, 7 to 8 inches long, in the Americas. The loggerhead shrike, widespread across the United States, more common in the South, and migrating only in the North, is gray with black in side of face, wings and tail. The similar, but paler and larger, northern shrike *(Lanius excubitor)* nests in northern Canada, visits the northern states in winter and feeds chiefly on mice and birds.

Starlings *(Family Sturnidae)*

In below-zero weather in the Midwest starlings *(Sturnus vulgaris)* are the only birds I've seen gather on a chimney top and warm themselves in the rising heat. This is an indication of the adaptability that has enabled this bird, introduced from Europe, to colonize across the continent. An aggressive species, it has increased at the expense of other species of similar nesting habits.

Farmlands with short grass or plowed fields for foraging and nearby trees with cavities for nesting seem optimum for starlings in summer when the birds are glossy black with yellow bills. In autumn they gather into flocks and roost in trees and in cattail marshes, and in winter, when they have moulted into a spangled plumage and the bill has turned black, some northern birds move southward and immense numbers may roost on towers and cornices of city buildings. The starling's food also varies seasonally: insects, cherries, seeds, and, at feeding stations, a great deal of suet.

The starling is a plump, short-tailed bird that walks with a waddling gait and flies with a swift, direct flight. Its song includes a variety of notes, some musical whistles, some less so, and some notes that seem imitations of other birds. The nests in tree cavities, woodpeckers nests, or crevices of a building contain four to six blue or bluish white eggs.

The starling family numbers many species in the Old World. Two have been introduced into America: the starling, mentioned above, and the crested myna (*Acridotheres cristatellus*) on Vancouver Island.

Vireos (*Family Vireonidae*)

Among the multitude of northbound warblers in spring the vireos are easy to overlook, for they are about the size of many female wood warblers, even duller in color, and just as troublesome to tell apart. The behavior of most species, however, contrasts with that of the warblers of the "flit and hop brigade," the vireos tending to be more leisurely in their movements and giving the impression of thoroughness as they hop among twigs and foliage looking for insects. The red-eyed vireo seems to reflect this deliberation in his singing, uttering short phrases with a rising inflection and brief pauses in between, phrases to which the following words have been put: "you see it—you know it—do you hear me—do you believe it?" However, not all vireos sing in this manner. The warbling vireo's song is a pleasing warble with an upward twist at the end. Nor are all vireos leisurely in behavior. The black-capped vireo of the Texas—Oklahoma arid scrub country, alert and energetic, dodges in and out of the foliage, from one twig to another.

The most distinctive character of the family is the vireo's nest, a firmly woven little basket hung from its edges in a flat fork of a tree or shrub. The inside and rim are neat, but the outside is often decorated with bits of lichen or birchbark caught up in cobwebs, as though to disguise it. The location varies from the treetops used by the warbling vireo to bushes used by the white-eyed vireo. The two to five eggs are white and may have small brown spots. The sexes are similar and are somewhat unusual among song-birds in that both sexes share incubation, the male of the red-eyed vireo singing while setting on the nest. Migration to winter quarters in the tropics is the rule, though some solitary vireos winter in the extreme southern states, and the Hutton's vireo of the Pacific coast area is a permanent resident there.

The vireo family is strictly New World, with eleven species nesting in the United States and Canada. They are small, insect-eating tree birds, 4 ¾ to 6 inches long. The bill is rather heavier than a warbler bill and has a slight hook at the tip. Vireo coloration is mostly dull olive, olive gray or gray on the upperparts and whitish variously tinged yellowish or grayish on the underparts. Pattern is usually restricted to wing bars, eye rings, and streaks through or above the eye.

Only four vireos, three of them common, have wide ranges. The red-eyed vireo (*Vireo olivaceus*) is the common vireo of the hardwood trees of the eastern half of the country and also extends to the northwestern part. Along with it in the northern forests of Canada lives the related Philadelphia vireo (*Vireo philadelphicus*). The solitary vireo (*Vireo solitarius*) is also a bird of the northern forests, but of mixed conifers and hardwoods, while the warbling vireo (*Vireo gilvus*) summers in the treetops across the country.

There are three common vireos of the eastern half of the United States only. The white-eyed vireo (*Vireo griseus*) is common and widespread in the shrubbery and thickets. In the Midwest, and overlapping the range of the white-eyed vireo, is the Bell's vireo (*Vireo bellii*), while the yellow-throated vireo (*Vireo flavifrons*) lives in tall trees of river edge, roadsides and villages.

There are four other vireos of limited distribution. The Hutton's vireo (*Vireo huttoni*), a permanent resident of the evergreen oaks of the Pacific coast area, the gray vireo (*Vireo vicinior*) of the hot open stands of pinyon and cedar and the dry chaparral of the Southwest, the black-capped vireo (*Vireo atricapilla*) ranging from Texas to Oklahoma, and the black-whiskered vireo (*Vireo altiloquus*) of mangrove areas of southern Florida.

Wood Warblers (*Family Parulidae*)

In early May of some years northbound migrating warblers arrive over-night in the Midwest in a great spectacular wave. Then every tree in a woodlot seems full of birds and each a different species. It is a bird watch-er's bonanza. In one hour one can see a dozen or more species of warblers. The males are in their brightly patterned breeding dress, con-trasting with the dull females and also with the dull winter dress of autumn migration, when their identification is the despair of bird watchers.

The wood warblers from a New World family of some 100 species of which 53 occur widely in the United States. All are migratory and most winter south into the tropics. Most of the species summer in the northern forests and the broadleafed forests of the East. Much of their migration funnels through the eastern states and the Mississippi Valley.

These birds are all small, 4 to 5 inches long, except for the "giant" yellow-breasted chat that, with its long tail, is 6½ inches long. These birds form a large part of the "hop and flit brigade" that gleans for insects on leaves and twigs of trees and shrubbery and snaps flying insects from the air. A very few feed on the forest floor or among reeds of marshes. Correlated with their insect food the bill is slender and fine pointed. In their winter home, however, they may eat much fruit.

Despite their name of warbler, the songs of many species are rather thin and wiry. The nest is usually cup-shaped and placed in a fork of a branch, rarely on the ground or in a hole. The three to six eggs are usually white or tinged blue or greenish and spotted brown.

The following is the arrangement of the 53 species included here: black and white warbler; prothonotary warbler; brown walking warblers, 5 species; golden and blue-winged warblers and relatives, 9 species; parula warbler and relatives, 3 species; tree warblers, 22 species; warblers of shrubbery and undergrowth, 9 species; and red-patterned warblers, 3 species.

BLACK AND WHITE WARBLER

Summering in the deciduous trees of the northern and eastern woodlands, the black and white warbler (*Mniotilta varia*) is the only one that has adopted the habits of a nuthatch, hopping along trunks and branches of trees in search of its insect food. This habit, and its black and white plumage with a white streak down the center of its black crown, makes identification easy. It migrates north early, a month or more before the main warbler migration, and its song is so high and thin that it is one of the first bird songs to become inaudible to the ears of aging ornithologists. The nest is placed on the ground, often at the base of a shrub and more or less concealed by dead leaves.

PROTHONOTARY WARBLER

Golden water warbler is the phrase often used to recall the prothonotary warbler's (*Protonotaria citrea*) appearance and its habitat. The bird is best seen from a punt or canoe poking along a waterway edged with mixed swamp forest, willows or cypress. The male prothonotary with glowing golden yellow head and underparts and contrasting olive back forages low among the bushes, on tree trunk and branch, on stranded logs and even on floating water plants. As he restlessly patrols his territory he may stop and sing or he may mount to a higher branch to deliver a loud, clear sweet song. An even sweeter song of several syllables followed by a varied warble is sometimes given in flight. The nest is unusual for a warbler, being placed in a hole, a low, natural cavity in a tree, an old woodpecker hole, a cranny in a bridge, or a bird box put up by man.

BROWN WALKING WARBLERS

There are five warblers that differ from their relatives in having plain brown or olive brown backs and in walking on the forest floor, instead of hopping in shrubbery or trees, in search of their food. The ovenbird (*Seiurus aurocapillus*), widespread in the dryer deciduous forests of the North and the East, is the best known because of its loud, easily recognized song increasing in volume with each phrase, "teacher-teacher-teacher," or variations such as "teacher-teachertea-chertea," all usually given from a perch found well up in a tree. But the ovenbird spends much of its time on the forest floor where the undergrowth is open and there is a plentiful litter of dead leaves. Here the nest is placed in a little depression and is roofed over with dead leaves, leaving only a tiny side entrance. The ovenbird's distinctive markings are the heavily streaked white underparts and the wide, golden, black-edged, central crown stripe.

Like the ovenbird but with a plain brown crown, a dark line through the eye and a light one above it, the two waterthrushes spend much of their time walking deliberately on the forest floor. They have the odd habit of teetering their tail up and down. The Louisiana waterthrush (*Seiurus motacilla*) favors shady edges of streams running through hardwood forests in the eastern United States. Its song is one of the outstanding warbler songs in which several loud musical preliminary notes are followed by a jumble of descending ones. The nest is tucked in a crevice in a bank or among the roots of an upturned tree. The northern waterthrush (*Seiurus noveboracensis*) is more boreal in distribution and it favors the edges of the quiet water of bogs and pools rather than running water.

Until the 1930's, when it was discovered in thickets in open forests in the highlands of the southern Allegheny Mountains, it used to be thought that the Swainson's warbler (*Limnothlypis swainsonii*) was restricted to wooded swamps and canebrakes along slow-moving streams of the Deep South. This bird is a rather tame, phlegmatic, slow-moving warbler which feeds on the ground. It may sing from the ground too or from a low perch, and its song, one of the outstanding warbler songs, is very loud and rich with a few deliberate notes quickening to a descending series that has been likened to a waterthrush song. The nest is placed in a low bush and the eggs are whitish and may have spots. The bird itself has a solid rufous crown, the underparts and face whitish except for a dark line through the eye and a pale one above it.

Olive-brown above, buffy white below, the worm-eating warbler (*Helmitheros vermivorus*) has its distinctive markings on the head: a pale central crown stripe bordered with black and a pale line over and a dark line through each eye. This bird summers in the eastern half of the United States. Cool shady wooded slopes, especially near small streams, are its favored habitats. Here the worm-eating warbler walks along, bobbing its head and carrying its tail high, looking for food among the fallen leaves. A shy and elusive bird, it is difficult to keep track of as it explores dark shady nooks. Unlike other brown warblers, its song is undistinguished, recalling the simple trill of a chipping sparrow. The nest, like that of the ovenbird, is on the ground and hidden beneath dead leaves.

Top: *Red-eyed vireo (Vireo olivaceus)*
Bottom: *Prothonotary warbler (Protonotaria citrea)*

GOLDEN-WINGED WARBLER,
BLUE-WINGED WARBLER AND RELATIVES

It is surprising that two species as different looking as the golden-winged and the blue-winged should hybridize. The male blue-winged warbler (*Vermivora pinus*) is brightly colored but with little pattern: head and underparts bright yellow, back and tail green, wing coverts blue with two white wing bars. The male golden-winged warbler (*Vermivora chrysoptera*) is dull in color, gray above, white below, with a bold pattern, yellow crown and wing patch, black patch on the side of the head outlined in white, and black throat.

Both species live in second growth and bushlands in the northeastern states and have similar habits and buzzing songs and make similar nests on or near the ground in shrubbery. The golden-winged warbler is the more northern, but its range overlaps with that of the blue-winged warbler, and it is here that hybridization occurs. These hybrids show an amazing range of variability and the extremes have been named: Lawrence's warbler with the yellow and olive coloration of the blue-winged plus the black markings of the golden-winged; and Brewster's warbler, colored like the golden-winged but without the black marks.

The related Bachman's warbler (*Vermivora bachmanii*) of the heavily timbered swamps of the Southeast is now the rarest warbler. Its history indicates violent changes in its status. Discovered in 1832, it was considered a lost species until the 1880's and 1890's when so many migrating birds were found that it was assumed to have become abundant. But the first nest was discovered only in 1906, and the last one in 1920. Only occasional birds have been seen in subsequent decades and it is now so rare that bird watchers anxious to put it on their life list have not been successful despite extensive searching. It is an easily recognized bird, the male being olive above except for black crown patch and yellow forehead, yellow on cheeks, and underparts yellow except for a large black patch on the throat.

The remaining six close relatives of the brightly colored, boldly patterned Bachman's warbler are obscurely patterned and predominantly olive and white or yellow, or gray and white. There are three species with olive-green backs: the northern nesting Tennessee warbler (*Vermivora peregrina*), the Nashville warbler (*Vermivora ruficapilla*), also a northern nester, and the orange-crowned warbler (*Vermivora celata*), chiefly a western bird. The other three species are birds of the arid West and South-

214

west and in keeping with their dryer habitat are predominantly gray and white: the Virginia's warbler (*Vermivora virginiae*) that summers in the scrub oaks of the mountains as far north as Utah; the Colima warbler (*Vermivora crissalis*) of Mexico and the extreme southwest of Texas in the rocky oak and maple clad tablelands; and last, Lucy's warbler (*Vermivora luciae*), summering north to Utah and Nevada, the only warbler nesting mainly in the hot deserts among the mesquite and cactus. It is also unusual because it sets its nest in a hole in a tree, either a natural hole or an old woodpecker nest.

PARULA WARBLER AND RELATIVES

The most remarkable thing about the parula warbler (*Parula americana*) is its nest site. It is in a streamer of moss draped on the branch of a tree so that the nest is slung as though in a hammock. Both the beard moss (*Usnea*) of the northeastern forests and the superficially similar Spanish moss (*Tillandsia*) of the trees of the Southeast are used to cradle the nests. Otherwise, like many tree warblers, the bird is typically one of the warblers that flit, hop and flutter among the twigs and leaves of forest and woodlot trees. Dainty and pretty are words that come to mind for the parula. A very small warbler, the back is blue with a yellowish saddlemark, the throat and breast yellow with a black and rufous bar across it. The related olive-backed warbler (*Parula pitiayumi*) of Mexico and the Rio Grande Valley is similar to the parula but with a black patch in its face and only a faint rusty band on the breast. Another Mexican warbler that crosses the border is the olive warbler (*Peucedramus taeniatus*). It summers in the open pine forests at high altitudes in southern New Mexico and Arizona and the male is very distinctly marked: gray and white except for the forepart of body and head which are buffy brown with a black streak through the eye.

TREE WARBLERS

The males of many of the twenty-two species of tree warblers of the genus *Dendroica* are brightly and intricately patterned in a fashion that gives each species distinctive markings which are difficult to memorize. There are such characteristics as wing bars, tail markings, rump, back and crown spots, face patterns, and streaking and patches on the underside. Coloration is black and white, yellow, orange, green, blue, gray, even brown. Their habitats range from treetops to shrubbery.

In the folowing pages two species, the yellow and the Kirtland's warbler, are treated individually and the remainder are grouped as northern, eastern, western, and southern tree warblers.

Yellow Warbler

The yellow warbler (*Dendroica petechia*) sings, "sweet, sweet, sweet, oh so sweet," from well-watered shrubbery of gardens and prairie rivers, arctic timberline, bushes bordering Canadian lakes, California rivers, Arizona irrigation ditches, and swamps and pastures of the eastern seaboard. It is the best-known and most widely distributed of the tree warblers, among which it is unusual in being bright yellow but without conspicuous markings. As with most warblers the time on its breeding grounds is short. The main spring arrival in the northern states from its wintering grounds, Mexico to South America, is in mid or late May, while the main southward migration is in late July or August. This leaves the birds little more than enough time to carry out the basic reproduction processes of nest building, egg laying, incubation and care of young which altogether take about forty-five days at a minimum, not including establishment of territory and courtship when the male may find time to sing as many as 3,240 songs in a day. He stops singing when he helps feed the young, but may sing again when parental cares are over.

The normal nest of the yellow warbler is a neat cup in a shrub. That social parasite, the cowbird, often lays eggs in the warbler's nest but the yellow warbler is not always a docile dupe. Sometimes it makes a new floor, burying the cowbird's eggs along with some of its own, and lays a new clutch. This may be repeated a number of times, making a several-storied nest.

Kirtland's Warbler

The Kirtland's warbler (*Dendroica kirtlandii*) contrasts with the yellow warbler in several ways. It has a very small summer range, measuring only 60 by 100 miles, all in the state of Michigan, and an estimated population of only 1,000 individuals, all of which winter in the Bahama Islands. The Kirtland's warbler also has very rigid breeding habitat requirements: it nests only in dense stands of second-growth jackpines that have sprung up after fires and are between five and fifteen feet high. This is a stage the pine stands pass through in about ten years, and poses special problems of

Yellow-breasted chat (Icteria virens)

management of habitats: to burn over selected areas so that there will always be second growth pine stands of the proper height if the species is to survive. It is a large, slow-moving warbler that both gleans through the pines and darts out for flying insects. The song is loud with a bubbling liquid quality and recalls at times the house wrens, or at times a water thrush song. The nest is well hidden on the ground. The male Kirtland's warbler is gray above and yellow on throat and breast with dark streaks on the back and on the sides of the breast.

Northern Tree Warblers

The nesting grounds of ten species of tree warblers lie in the great transcontinental forest bands of spruce and fir, birch, maple and aspen, that extend from New England and eastern Canada to Alaska. All ten of these warblers nest in the eastern half of the country, but farther west species drop out until only two, the myrtle and the blackpoll, reach northwestern Alaska. Nine of these warblers migrate only through the eastern United States. The tenth, the myrtle warbler, also migrates through the West. A few, such as the palm and myrtle warblers, winter in the extreme southern United States; others, such as the blackpoll, winter as far south as South America. Some of them are among our brightest patterned warblers.

These ten species are as follows: the Magnolia warbler (*Dendroica magnolia*), the Cape May warbler (*Dendroica tigrina*), the black-throated blue warbler (*Dendroica caerulescens*), the myrtle warbler (*Dendroica coronata*), the black-throated green warbler (*Dendroica virens*), the blackburnian warbler (*Dendroica fusca*), the chestnut-sided warbler (*Dendroica pensylvanica*), the bay-breasted warbler (*Dendroica castanea*), the blackpoll warbler (*Dendroica striata*) and the palm warbler (*Dendroica palmarum*).

Eastern Tree Warblers

The four tree warblers that nest only in the eastern half of the United States differ greatly in habitat preference and include one of the dullest tree warblers. This is the pine warbler (*Dendroica pinus*). It is olive above, dull yellow below, with a pale line over the eye and two wing bars. As its name implies, it is a bird of stands of tall pines. Many spend the winter in the southern states and these feed closer to the ground and sometimes even on the ground. The cerulean warbler (*Dendroica cerulea*), blue above, white below, with a black throat band and streaks on its flanks, favors the treetops of river bottom woodlands. The yellow-throated warbler (*Dendroica dominica*), mostly gray and white with a yellow throat, prefers oaks and cypress draped with Spanish moss in the South and sycamores farther north. The prairie warbler (*Dendroica discolor*), with a rufous patch on olive back, yellow breast and two black lines in its yellow face, seeks dryer, second growth except in the extreme South where it is a permanent resident in coastal mangroves.

Western Tree Warblers

There are four tree warblers that nest only in the West: the Audubon's warbler (*Dendroica auduboni*); the Townsend's warbler (*Dendroica townsendi*), the western counterpart of the black-throated green warbler; the related hermit warbler (*Dendroica occidentalis*); and the black-throated gray warbler (*Dendroica nigrescens*).

Southern Tree Warblers

There are two tree warblers of limited distribution in the South. One is Grace's warbler (*Dendroica graciae*), whose summer range centers in the pine forests of the mountains of Arizona and New Mexico. It is the counterpart of the yellow-throated warbler of the eastern forests, but it is smaller and lacks the black face patch and white ear markings. The other is the

Prairie warblers (Dendroica discolor)

golden-cheeked warbler (*Dendroica chrysoparia*), which summers only in the cedars of south central Texas. It is the local representative of the black-throated green warbler of the North, but differs in having crown, back and side of neck as well as throat black, throwing into contrast the golden cheeks with a black line through the eye.

WARBLERS OF SHRUBBERY AND UNDERGROWTH

The nine warblers grouped here summer in shrubbery, in thickets and in woodland undergrowth. Some nest only in the East, some in the North, some in the West and some are widespread. Plain olive above and yellow below is the basic coloration of most species, with bold black or slaty patterns of varying extent on head and neck in the males. One species, however, the Canada warbler, has the back gray. There are the Kentucky warbler and its relatives, the hooded warbler and its relatives, the yellow-throat, and the yellow-breasted chat.

Kentucky Warbler and Relatives

Unlike many ground birds that have inconspicuous brown coloration, the male Kentucky warbler (*Oporornis formosus*) is as bright as a tree warbler but with a simple pattern: yellow underparts and green upperparts, black forehead and cheeks with a yellow line from bill over the eye that curls around behind it. This bird spends much of its time walking on the ground, poking into crevices and crannies, looking under leaves and examining twigs for its insect food. It is found in the wetter, shady woodlands of the eastern central states. There it may perch in the low shrubby undergrowth to sing its loud, whistled series of notes. Its song and color are both conspicuous, to which it adds a habit of quarreling with its neighbors, and the males are continually chasing each other through the undergrowth. The three related warblers (the males with slaty and gray head, neck and breast) are different in appearance and habits, living shy, elusive lives in the shrubbery of forest edge. They are: Macgillivray's warbler (*Oporornis tolmiei*) of the West, the mourning warbler (*Oporornis philadelphia*) of the North, and the Connecticut warbler (*Oporornis agilis*) of central Canada.

Hooded Warbler and Relatives

The hooded warbler (*Wilsonia citrina*) begins to sing his loud, clear, sprightly phrases while on his way north from wintering in Central America. In his summer home he continues a persistent songster in the undergrowth of shrubs and saplings of shady woodlands and swampy forests of the eastern United States. In habits he is active and restless, as much a flycatcher as a gleaner of insects from twigs and leaves, and he continually fans his tail to show the concealed white markings. Retiring, even shy, he is not always easy to see, but even so one can keep track of him by his singing as he patrols his territory. His pattern is simple and bold: the bright yellow forehead and cheeks are enclosed by the black hood covering the crown, sides of neck and throat, a pattern not even approached by any other warbler. Otherwise he is olive green above and bright yellow below. The related Canada warbler (*Wilsonia canadensis*) summers in the forest undergrowth in the Northeast and the Wilson's warbler (*Wilsonia pusilla*), in forest edge in the North and the mountains of the West.

Yellowthroat

The first warbler I learned to recognize, even before I knew warblers had names, was a yellow-green bird with a black mask that lived in a raspberry patch by an old orchard. It was, of course, a male yellowthroat (*Goethlypis trichas*) that came up through the leaves peering and flitting, scolding and chattering, hopping out, tail cocked up, fluttering, disappearing and poking its head out somewhere else. Inevitably these antics recall those of a wren. But the song, quite unlike a wren's, is an easily recognized "witchety, witchety, witchety," heard from thicket and tangle, by pond or stream or in meadow or marsh over much of the United States in spring. The related ground-chat (*Chamaethlypis poliocephala*) of Mexico occurs as far north as the lower Rio Grande Valley in Texas.

Yellow-breasted Chat

The song of the yellow-breasted chat (*Icteria virens*), unlike that of any other bird, is a medley of loud whistles, rattles, cackles, organ notes and squawks. Along prairie rivers it sings from the cottonwood trees and when anyone approaches it flies down into the low dense shrubbery to be seen no more, though it can be heard clucking and scolding. In the thickets and tangles of eastern meadows the male may sing from a low perch and sometimes during a grotesque, dangling flight from one thicket to the next. The yellow-breasted chat recalls the yellow-throat in its choice of habitat, retiring habits, scolding of an intruder, olive upperparts and yellow breast. But the chat is much larger—6½ inches long—has a longer tail, and it has only a black patch in front of the eye instead of a complete mask.

RED-PATTERNED WARBLERS

There are three warblers with conspicuous red in the plumage: two redstarts and the red-faced warbler. One need not leave the city to see these warblers. One of the attractions of a Chicago restaurant is the tree-shaded sunken patio where, spring and autumn, migrating warblers pause. The most showy of these is the American redstart (*Setophaga ruticilla*) in which the male is mostly black with six splashes of red—two in the tail, one in each wing and one on each side of the breast. The less gaudy female has the black and red replaced by olive and yellow. Living below the main canopy of the treetops, the redstart flits or hovers to pick an insect off a leaf, from a twig or bark and then chases a flying insect with a twisting, turning flight, fairly dancing through the air with a weightless, sprightly grace. Then it pauses a moment with fanned tail and drooping wings to show its salmon spots. The redstart is one of the most common birds of the deciduous woodlands of the eastern and northern forests. In the tropics where it winters, its Spanish name, candelilla, means "little torch."

The related painted redstart (*Setophaga picta*) of the oaks of the southwestern mountains is similar to the redstart but with white in wings and tail and the whole breast red. The only other United States warbler that has red color is the red-faced warbler (*Cardellina rubrifrons*) of limited distribution in upland coniferous forests of the Southwest. It is gray above, white below, with red forehead, cheeks and throat and a black band across the crown.

Weaverbird Family (*Family Ploceidae*)

One morning a house sparrow (*Passer domesticus*) turned up in my garage but instead of fluttering about the ceiling and the window as a house wren had done the week before, the sparrow quickly flew down and crept out through a crevice under the door. Obviously adapted to getting along with man, the house sparrow is a bold and impudent bird as well as a suspicious and wary one. It has had a long history of association with man in Europe and Asia and this has continued since its introduction into America in the 1850's in the New York area. It now occurs in practically all well-settled areas from southern Canada to Mexico.

The man-sparrow relationship has fluctuated. The bird was introduced to help combat an insect pest but as it became extremely abundant and interfered with native nesting birds it became detested on economic, aesthetic and even moral grounds. Now that its numbers have decreased in city and town, correlated with the decrease in horse-drawn transportation and in horse manure, from which the sparrows picked grain, we are able to view the sparrow as another element in our bird life.

The house sparrow is a noisy, gregarious bird feeding on the seeds, grains and scraps on the ground about houses and fields, and enlivening even the winter scene with its presence. It nests in crevices and corners about buildings and in nearby hollow trees, sometimes making its bulky oval nest in tree branches. In the autumn, flocks may visit grain fields but winter sees them back around settlement.

The weaverbird family is a large Old World family with two species introduced into America. The house sparrow, 6 inches long, is a stout bird, the male with a gray crown and a black bib. The female is duller, with streaked upperparts and dingy white underparts. The related European tree sparrow (*Passer montanus*), also an introduction, is similar to the house sparrow but has a chestnut crown and a black spot on its white cheeks.

Meadowlarks, Blackbirds, Orioles, and Others (*Family Icteridae*)

Wherever there are members of the blackbird family they are likely to be conspicuous to eye and ear. Bobolinks fly singing over grassy hayfields; meadowlarks sit up on fence posts or stand in the short grass where the sun brightens their yellow breasts; blackbirds and grackles squeal or sing by the treeful in the spring, and in autumn great flocks are a part of the landscape; and orange-yellow orioles let their golden notes drop down a they fly from treetop to treetop.

The blackbirds are an exclusively American family of 94 species o which 20 occur in the United States. They are from 7 to 17 inches long some feed on the ground, some in marshes, others in trees. Their bill are strong and their diet is omnivorous, including a wide variety of insects seeds, grain and berries. The type of nest varies greatly from a cup-shaped or a domed nest on the ground or an open nest in reeds or trees to a pensile sac-like nest. An exception is the cowbirds, who are parasites using the nests of other birds.

The arrangement of the species is: bobolink, meadowlarks, grackles, red winged blackbird, cowbird and orioles.

BOBOLINK

Spring is not complete in the northern states until the male bobolinks (*Dolichonyx oryzivorus*) are perching on fence posts and chasing the females over the grass tops of meadow and hayfield, singing their hurried jumble o bubbling, metallic notes as they go. Most birds are dark above, pale below but the spring male bobolink reverses this and wears his colors upside down being a black bird with white and yellow in his upperparts. His mate i quite different—a buffy, sparrowy-streaked bird. She builds the nest or the ground among grass stems. By the time the young have grown and the males have moulted into their female-like winter plumage, the bird all across the northern part of the country are gathering into great flock and setting out for their wintering grounds in southern South America The bobolink is a small blackbird, 6-8 inches long, and while his summer diet is insects, like that of some of his relatives, he changes his diet to one of seeds and grain in the autumn. When rice growing flourished in the Carolinas the bobolink was considered a major rice-eating pest.

MEADOWLARKS

As the meadowlark walks away in the grass, the streaked brown pattern of its back matches the grass in which it lives. When it turns to face a viewer, the yellow breast with a black neck band make it strikingly conspic uous. Actually there are two species, the eastern meadowlark (*Sturnella magna*) and the western meadowlark (*Sturnella neglecta*), and between

Western meadowlark (Sturnella neglecta)

them they occupy most of the temperate zone grasslands of the continent. The two birds differ in appearance only in small details of plumage, but the songs are quite different, that of the eastern bird being a whistled series of a few sweet notes while that of the western bird is a richer, fuller, lower song recalling in quality that of a thrush. Both are grassland birds, both make a domed grass nest on the ground and both are permanent residents over much of their ranges, only withdrawing from the extreme northern part of their range after they have gathered in loose flocks.

COMMON GRACKLE AND RELATIVES

The pale yellow eyes of common grackles (*Quiscalus quiscula*) give them a sinister appearance. They do eat bird's eggs and young birds at times, but I welcome them to my garden for the variety of bird behavior they have shown me. One takes an acorn in its bill and rotates it against the horny keel in the roof of its beak, like a can-opener blade, so the shell falls in two pieces and the nut meat can be bitten to pieces and swallowed. Several times, when dry bread was put out for them, the birds dunked these in a bird bath, softening them before eating them. Having seen a grackle on an ant hill rubbing ants on its feathers (a strange activity called "anting") and going through the same procedure with a piece of orange peel, we put moth balls on the lawn and, sure enough, several grackles picked them up and went through "anting" motions. So far, the activity has not been explained. Equally remarkable was the way one pair raised their young in a nest placed on top of a house sparrow's nest in a vine on a garage.

In the eastern half of the country the common grackle is a common, conspicuous, noisy bird of open country and trees, farmland, swamps and marshes, the water's edge, gardens and city parks where it walks about on the ground or perches in trees feeding on as wide a variety of food as the crow. Large insects, seeds and nuts are perhaps the staples, but minnows, frogs, small birds and corn are among the other items eaten. Urban birds rummage through trash baskets and eat garbage. The spring song is a rusty squawk given as the bird fluffs out the body feathers and half spreads wings and tail. Solitary or in colonies, the bulky cup-shaped nest is placed in the top of a conifer, in other trees, bushes, in the willows or reeds of swamps, in natural tree cavities, or crevices around buildings. In the summer roosts, scores of birds gather in shade trees, later to merge into larger roosts until the winter roost contains thousands, even hundreds of thousands, of birds and the flocks are conspicuous elements in the landscape. Northern birds withdraw southward in winter.

The common grackle is 11-14 inches long, a glossy black bird with a long wedge-shaped tail in the male. The related boat-tailed grackle (*Cassidix mexicanus*) of the coastal marshes of the southeastern coasts and waterways is a larger bird, 16-17 inches long, with a smaller, brownish female. Two smaller relatives are the rusty blackbird (*Euphagus carolinus*) nesting in wooded swamps from New England to Alaska and wintering in the Southeast, and the Brewer's blackbird (*Euphagus cyanocephalus*), widespread in the West, with northern birds wintering south to Mexico.

REDWINGED BLACKBIRD AND OTHER MARSH RELATIVES

A leafless tree full of blackbirds in a northern spring gives as joyous a sound during the day as does a pond full of tree frogs and spring peepers by night. The redwinged blackbirds (*Agelaius phoeniceus*) are not yet in full song but the clicking and clucking and squealing and the snatches of song make up a chorus to which rusty blackbirds, Brewer's blackbirds and grackles may contribute. Indeed, in watching the passage of great flocks and lines of blackbirds one is sometimes disconcerted to find that parties of several species, blackbirds and grackles, and even starlings are flying and feeding more or less together.

The redwing ranges from southern Canada to Mexico and is a resident except in the more northern parts. When the birds arrive in the North they come in flocks that at first feed in the fields and spend the night in the dead last-year's cattails. But as the new cattails grow up the males stake out territories in the marsh and then the females join the males, mate, and build their deep-cup nests among the new cattails. Male and female used to spend much of the day in the marshes, but in recent years it has been found that in the Midwest more and more redwings are nesting in grassy fields, apparently a new habitat for them. After the nesting season the birds flock again but may stay in the marshes, inconspicuous while they shed all their tail feathers at once and the new ones grow in. Most birds moult and replace their tail feathers a pair at a time so the tail will continue as a steering and balancing organ. But the redwing and certain other "blackbirds" seem able to get along without this for a time in early autumn. Later with full length tails the birds feed in the fields and swarm to community roosts.

The widespread red-winged blackbird, 7 to 9 inches long, has the male black with red and orange epaulettes, the female with a dark sparrowy streaked plumage. The related tricolored blackbird (*Agelaius tricolor*) with red and white epaulettes breeds in great colonies in marshes in the interior valleys of California. Even more different, the yellow-headed blackbird (*Xanthocephalus xanthocephalus*) has the male black with yellow head and shoulders and with white in the wings. It breeds in marshes of the eastern half of the country and winters south into Mexico.

COWBIRDS

The dark birds with rather stubby bills that walk along with grazing cattle or horses are cowbirds. They are catching the insects the grazing beasts stir into activity, an easier way for the birds to get their food than by searching out each hidden insect. This is not a new habit: the old-time buffalo hunters knew the brown-headed cowbird (*Molothrus ater*) as a companion of the buffalo and called it the buffalo bird. Like other members of the blackbird family, with which it sometimes flocks and with which it has some habits in common, the cowbird varies its diet with fruit, seeds and grain in season. It does not make a nest and raise its young but lays

its eggs in other birds' nests and leaves the eggs to be hatched and the young to be raised by foster parents, of which more than 200 species have been recorded. The brown-headed cowbird, 6-8 inches long, is a black bird with a brown head and neck; the female is slaty gray. Its range is continent-wide; it is migratory in the north. The related bronzed cowbird (*Tangavius aeneus*) of the Mexican border is a more uniformly dark bird.

ORIOLES

Among the most brilliant of our birds, the orioles live in treetops where they search for insects among the leaves and branches, sing their whistled songs and harsh chattering notes and weave their semipensile, cup-shaped or sac-shaped nests in which they lay three to seven whitish to bluish, brown-marked eggs. Seasonally the diet changes from insects and nectar to fruit, and in winter the orioles migrate to the tropics. The males of all eight species, 6 to 9 inches long, are boldly patterned in black and yellow, orange or chestnut. The females are quite different, mostly olive and yellow birds with little pattern.

The orange and black Baltimore oriole (*Icterus galbula*), with the whole head and neck black, summers in the eastern part of the country in shade trees and woodlots and is replaced in the western part of the country by the Bullock's oriole (*Icterus bullockii*), also orange and black but with the black of head and throat interrupted by the orange of side of head and neck. It lives in cottonwoods, oaks and other riparian trees. These two orioles are so closely related that where both occur hybridization may take place. In the lowlands of central California east to south Texas the Bullock's oriole may share the trees along the watercourses with the hooded oriole (*Icterus cucullatus*), an orange and black Mexican species with the head orange except for the black throat. The preference of the hooded oriole for palm fibers in its nest construction and its habit of sewing its deep cup-shaped nest to the underside of fan palm leaves have given it the name of palm leaf oriole. It also has a fondness for nectar and a tolerance for humans. Thus the ornamental palms and flowering shrubs planted in city parks and gardens have provided new habitats for this familiar bird.

There are five other orioles. Two of them are orange and black, each of limited distribution in the United States. The spotted-breasted oriole (*Icterus pectoralis*) of Central America, with a black-spotted breast, has been introduced and established in the Miami area of Florida. The Lich-

Baltimore oriole (Icterus galbula)

tenstein's oriole (*Icterus gularis*) of Mexico ranges north to southeastern Texas. There are also two black and yellow orioles, the black-headed oriole (*Icterus graduacauda*) of Mexico and southeastern Texas and the Scott's oriole (*Icterus parisorum*) of northern Mexico and the southwestern United States in the semi-arid lower mountain slopes, mesas and plateaus where pinyon pines, junipers and yuccas grow. The fifth species, the orchard oriole (*Icterus spurius*) of the eastern and central United States, is a black and chestnut bird.

Tanagers *(Family Thraupidae)*

The tanagers are notable for the brilliance of the male plumage and a song that is robin-like in phrasing but often with a certain hoarseness. There are more than two hundred tanagers in the American tropics but only four come north of the Mexican border, and then only as summer visitors. They spend much of their time among the foliage of the treetops, moving about deliberately, in summer seeking caterpillars and other insects. The bright males are often as difficult to see as the dull yellow-green females. Sometimes they vary their routine by flying out to snatch a flying insect from the air. Rarely one may see them among the tree trunks along a forested trail. The open nest is in a fork of a branch, and three to five greenish blue spotted eggs are laid in it. While the male does not share in incubation he does help care for the young. With the ripening of fruits and berries tanagers feed on them, and this constitutes their diet in their winter homes in the tropics.

The four tanagers of the United States are tree birds about 7 to 8 inches long with rather stout bills. The scarlet tanager (*Piranga olivacea*) of the eastern forests has the male red with black wings and tail. The summer tanager (*Piranga rubra*) of woodlands from California to the southeastern states is all red. The hepatic tanager (*Piranga flava*) is a tropical species that ranges north to Arizona and Texas and is red with dark ear coverts and bill. The western tanager (*Piranga ludoviciana*) summering from Alaska to California has an orange-red head and a black and yellow body and black wings and tail. The females are all much more alike, greenish above, yellowish below.

Sparrows, Buntings, Finches and their Relatives (*Family Fringillidae*)

Many of the sparrow family are streaked brownish birds of obscure habits, but there are also brilliant and boldly marked males of some species. Among the songs of both brilliant and dull birds are some of our favorites. Whatever many species of this family may lack in appeal, they make up in numbers. With some 78 species, it is the largest family in America. Some are mainly tree birds; others live in shrubbery and grassland, from marsh, desert, tundra and mountaintops to dooryards. There are a host of vernacular names for them: cardinal, grosbeak, bunting, finch, redpoll, siskin, crossbill, dickcissel, towhee, junco, longspur and seedeater—all evidence of their impact on the popular consciousness. However, what may be the best-known "sparrow," the house sparrow, belongs to another family, the weaverbirds.

The sparrows are adapted for seed eating in having a conical bill, pointed at the tip for picking up tiny bits of food and heavy at the base for cracking seeds. Like most birds however, their diet is varied and in season insects are eaten and fed to the young. Fruits and tender vegetation are used as food. Some species are permanent residents, others move only far enough south to find seeds available, and their winter flocks are commonly seen along weedy roadsides and open fields. Other species migrate to the tropics for the winter and a few go as far as South America.

The birds usually pair, make a cup-shaped nest in tree, shrub, on the ground or in a hollow in a bank or in a crevice in a rock. The two to six eggs, white or tinted, plain or spotted or marbled, are laid in the nest and here the young are raised.

The sparrow family is treated here in three main groups: tropical grosbeaks and buntings; northern grosbeaks and finches; and American sparrows.

TROPICAL GROSBEAKS AND RELATED BUNTINGS

These grosbeaks and buntings are birds of the trees and shrubbery though they sometimes feed on the ground. The males are richly colored, either mostly red or blue with little pattern or boldly patterned, suggesting the

231

tropics to the south where many close relatives live. The females are dull and only two species have a streaked sparrowy pattern. Except for the cardinals, these birds winter in the tropics. There are nine species ranging from 5½ to 8½ inches long.

Cardinals

The cardinal (*Richmondena cardinalis*) is a popular bird of dooryard shrubbery and lawns. It is the state bird of Delaware, Illinois, Indiana, Kentucky and West Virginia, and its red color and crested shape make it a favorite decoration for Christmas cards, painted chinaware and calendars.

Unlike the other tropical grosbeaks, the cardinals are permanent residents of hedgerows, shrubbery and thickets of forest edge, fields, farms and gardens. It ranges from Mexico to southern California, Arizona and the eastern half of the United States, where it has extended its range northward to eastern Canada in recent years.

In winter cardinals come to bird feeding stations for seeds. In earliest spring in the Northeast the male mounts to the tops of still leafless maples and gives its distinctive, pleasing song: a series of loud whistled notes uttered rapidly and rhythmically. Soon it begins to defend its territory and its pugnacity even finds expression in shadow-boxing its reflection in window glass. As part of courtship the male feeds his mate, who is browner, but also crested. Later he helps feed the young even when they are out of the nest and look much like the brown female, but with a dark bill.

The related pyrrhuloxia (*Pyrrhuloxia sinuata*), a grosbeak of Mexico, extends north into the southwestern states. While in general cardinal-like, it has a shorter, stubby bill and the male has much gray in flanks and upperparts.

Rose-breasted and Black-headed Grosbeaks

When the new leaves are tinging the northern deciduous forests with spring green, and the migrating warblers are swarming, the rose-breasted grosbeak (*Pheucticus ludovicianus*) arrives back from its winter home in tropical America to take up residence in the trees of second growth woods and open deciduous woodlands in the eastern and northern part of the country. The male is a striking bird: black and white with a rose-red breast. His mate is streaked brown and white. The song is a melodious series of

232

Top: Blue grosbeak (Guiraca caerulea)
Bottom: Cardinal (Richmondena cardinalis)

phrases that follow each other so closely as almost to merge into a warble, and recalls a robin's song with the phrases run together. Usually, in birds where the male is much brighter than the female, only the female incubates. But the rose-breasted grosbeak is an exception. The male not only incubates but also sings while sitting on the nest in some low tree.

The related black-headed grosbeak (*Pheucticus melanocephalus*) that summers in the open woodlands of the Rocky Mountains and westward is similar but with buffy orange underparts.

Blue Grosbeak and Buntings

The males of these grosbeaks and buntings are vividly colored, but the blue ones, seen at a distance, or in a poor light, appear as drab as their dull mates. All live in shrubbery, thickets and tangles of second growth, and nest there. They are inobtrusive and most of those that I have seen have been hopping in the shrubbery, darting away into forest or brush, or perched singing on a low treetop or telephone wire.

Seen in good light, the male blue grosbeak (*Guiraca caerulea*), 6½ inches long, of the southern part of the country, and the indigo bunting (*Passerina cyanea*), 4½ inches long, of the eastern and central states are both generally blue. The male Lazuli bunting (*Passerina amoena*) of the western states is paler blue with rusty breast and white belly. The male varied bunting (*Passerina versicolor*) of Mexico ranges into adjacent American states and is generally purplish. The females of all three are brownish. More distinctive is the fifth species, the painted bunting (*Passerina ciris*) of the southern states, with blue head, green back, and red rump and underparts; its female is greenish, somewhat yellower below.

NORTHERN GROSBEAKS AND FINCHES, etc.

Most of these northern birds have some yellow or red in the male's plumage—not the screaming colors of the tropics but more sober shades that harmonize with the coniferous forests and northern barrens where many of them live in the Old World and the New. There are sixteen species, ranging from 4 to 9 inches long, in the United States and Canada. Southward migration in winter is limited and flocks of some species wander widely and irregularly in search of food.

Evening Grosbeak

The arrival of a flock of evening grosbeaks (*Hesperiphona vespertina*) at a

234

feeding station is the high point of the year for some bird watchers in northern states. While some of these big, clumsy-looking birds crowd the feeding tray shelling sunflower seeds, the others sit stolidly in a nearby tree awaiting their turn. These birds have a healthy appetite and the amount of seeds they can eat may cause a surprising drain on the food budget.

The presence of evening grosbeaks in the Northeast is recent. Within historical times their eastern outpost was Lake Superior. By the mid-part of the present century, the birds had extended their earlier range, the coniferous forests of the western mountains and the Boreal Zone, to New England. Winter flocks have appeared, sporadically as far south as Kentucky. Two factors may have influenced this: the planting about farms and ranches of the box elder trees whose seeds are their favorite foods, and the increase in feeding stations supplying sunflower seeds, insuring winter survival.

House finch (Carpodacus mexicanus)

Purple and House Finches

The house finch (*Carpodacus mexicanus*), 6 inches long, is a sparrowy streaked bird, the male with a red crown, breast and rump. It is common and conspicuous in the lowlands of California, Arizona and western Mexico and takes its name from its habit of foraging in urban alleys and nesting in crannies about buildings as well as foraging in the desert and nesting in cactus and mesquite.

Similar to the house finch, but with the male more raspberry-tinged red and lacking dark flank streaks, the purple finch (*Carpodacus purpureus*) has a quite different habitat. Its summer home is in the coniferous forest of the north and the mid-altitudes of the mountains. In winter it moves to more southern and settled areas and comes freely to bird feeding stations for seed. They are so similar to house sparrows in size and form that the females may be mistaken for them at a glance that does not note the streaked underparts of the female purple finch. As spring approaches, the males start to sing their loud, rich warble, sometimes before they leave for their nesting grounds. The Cassin's finch (*Carpodacus cassinii*) is a western species, nesting at higher altitudes in the mountains, and is so like the purple finch that sight identification is difficult.

Pine Grosbeak

I have two particularly vivid memories of pine grosbeaks (*Pinicola enucleator*). One is of a rosy-colored bird sitting in the February sunshine on a snow-covered spruce branch within a few feet of me and singing its whisper song; the other is of these birds feeding on the apple blossoms in a French-Canadian orchard, the males pausing now and then to give their full-scale songs of trills and warbles. The pine grosbeak is a plump, slow-moving bird, 8 inches long, that goes in flocks in the northern and western mountain coniferous forest most of the year. In winter a few move into our northern states. The male, 8 inches long, is rose pink with dark rump and tail and gray belly; the female has the red replaced with yellowish olive and gray.

Rosy Finches

Only climbers who reach the highest parts of our western mountains see rosy finches in their breeding grounds. Nests are placed in crevices, niches and caves of precipitous cliffs, and the birds come down to walk and hop

Evening grosbeak (*Hesperiphona vespertina*)

on the alpine meadows looking for seeds and insects, and glean over the
melting snowbanks for the wind-blown food items accumulated there. Since
nest and food supply may be far apart these birds have evolved cheek
pouches for carrying food to their young

Severe snowstorms in early winter send the birds by the thousands down
ward to the lower levels, high plateaus, and plains. Here they feed on the
ground or snow on weed and grass seeds and at night roost in rock crevices
abandoned cliff swallow nests, and may substitute crannies about ranch
houses for rock crevice dormitories.

There are three rosy finches, 6-7 inches long, brownish or blackish
unstreaked birds with some pink especially in the wings of the males: the
brown-capped rosy finch (*Leucosticte australis*) of the Wyoming-New
Mexico mountains; the black rosy finch (*Leucosticte atrata*) of the central
Rocky Mountains, a much darker bird with a black and gray crown; and
the gray-crowned rosy finch (*Leucosticte tephrocotis*) ranging from Cali
fornia to Alaska.

Redpolls

When snow blankets the countryside in the northern states, the redpolls
arrive from the Arctic. In flocks of scores and hundreds they feed with
incessant twittering in the open weedy fields. Like many northern finches
they are restless and the whole flock may swirl up and about, to alight
nearby and continue eating seeds. Again, like some other northern finches
there may be an uncertainty in their occurrence in winter: abundant one
year, scarce the next. They are small birds, 5 inches long, streaked brownish and whitish. The male with his red crown, black chin and rosy breast
is a handsome bird. The common redpoll (*Acanthis flammea*) is the
species that is usual in the northern states in winter. But the bird enthu-
siasts will scan each flock for paler birds with white unstreaked rumps. They
will be the hoary redpoll (*Acanthis hornemanni*) that comes so far south
only rarely. Both nest on the Arctic tundra.

Goldfinches and Siskin

A black and yellow bird feeding at a summer thistle head and then flying
away with bounding flight and cheerful calls of "per-chic-er-re" and lighting
in top of a tree or a shrub; this is the male American goldfinch (*Spinus
tristis*) in its summer dress and in his favorite habitat, shared with his olive

green mate. This goldfinch is one of the last birds to start nesting, perhaps to take advantage of the summer crop of weed seeds as food for the young. When the young have grown to independence the goldfinches gather into flocks and search weedy fields and thickets of alder and birch for the seeds these trees bear. But the male is now in brownish olive winter dress, very like the females.

The American goldfinch, 4½ inches long, breeds across the northern half of the country, and while some stay north and even join flocks of siskins and redpolls, many move southward as far as Mexico. The male of the related lesser goldfinch (*Spinus psaltria*) of the western states has either a green or a black back, while the Lawrence's goldfinch (*Spinus lawrencei*) of the dryer part of California and southward has a black area about the bill and a gray back. The pine siskin (*Spinus pinus*) is a much plainer, more streaked bird of the northern forests across the continent. The European goldfinch (*Carduelis carduelis*), introduced in several localities with indifferent success, has a distinctive head pattern of red, black and white.

Crossbills

Red males, yellow-orange young and yellow-olive females make up the wandering flocks of crossbills whose colors harmonize so well with the deep green needles of the northern coniferous trees which are the normal haunts of these birds. The crossed tip of the mandibles is a special adaptation for prying apart the scales of spruce, fir and pine cones so the tongue can scoop out the seeds, the staple food of the crossbills. Rather bold and deliberate in actions as they climb about the twigs, a crossbill may even dangle upside down as it extracts seeds from a cone, or it may snip off a cone, carry it to a better perch, and hold it with one foot as it gets out the seed.

Crossbills are irregular in occurrence and erratic in breeding time. This correlates with the cone crop locally; if it is good, the birds may arrive in abundance, begin breeding even in midwinter, and continue breeding even into summer, when insects, of which aphids seem favorites, are also utilized as food. But if the cone crop fails, the crossbills may desert a whole area and be absent for years. At irregular intervals invasions of crossbills may occur far south of their normal range.

There are two species: the white-winged crossbill (*Loxia leucoptera*) with two conspicuous white wing bars, and of northern distribution across

American goldfinch (Spinus tristis)

the continent; and the red crossbill (*Loxia curvirostra*) without wing bars, which is of somewhat more southern distribution and also ranges in the western mountains.

AMERICAN SPARROWS

This is by far the largest group of "sparrows" and includes most of the dull, brown-streaked species. It has many relatives in South America and a few in Eurasia where they are known as buntings. The species in the United States and Canada are mostly ground-feeding birds, some of the shrubbery-grassland edge, some of the grasslands, and a few of the tundra. Most of them have a streaked back, brown, black, gray and tan with a dead-grass pattern. In some the underparts are also streaked and to differentiate among some species needs careful scrutiny. A few species, such as the towhees, juncos and seedeaters, have bolder patterns, and some of the sparrow-streaked birds have conspicuous head markings as on the crowned sparrows. Sexual dimorphism varies; it is hardly evident in many streaked sparrows but pronounced in the black and white lark bunting, which moults into a female-like sparrowy plumage in winter. Migration is only of moderate extent in many species and the weedy fields of the temperate zone accommodate a great many sparrowy birds in winter; the dickcissel, however, migrates in great flocks to tropical America for the winter. There are 52 species in America, ranging in size from 4 to 9 inches long.

Towhees

Among the dead leaves beneath a dry roadside thicket the rufous-sided towhee (*Pipilo erythrophthalmus*) works vigorously and noisily. With jump-kicks it uses both feet at once to scratch away the leaves in its search for the insects and seeds underneath. Alarmed, the bird flits away into the shrubbery, the white tips to the black tail feathers showing conspicuously and signaling its identity. When the male mounts to a low perch, branch or shrub top he sings his distinctive "drink-your-tea," and one sees the rufous flanks that have given this bird the folk name of "ground robin" in the Northeast. The rufous-sided towhee is the most widespread of the four towhees. It is a resident of most of the shrubbery country across the United States except in the extreme north, where it summers only, and some of the Central states, where it occurs only in winter.

The four towhees are large, stout, rather long-tailed sparrows, 8-9 inches long, that feed on the ground in the edge of shrubbery. The male rufous-sided towhee is black, white and rufous. The green-tailed towhee (*Chlorura chlorura*) of the western states is grayish with green wings and tail, rufous crown, and a white throat. The brown towhee (*Pipilo fuscus*) of the Far West and Southwest is generally brown, and in addition to living in arid native brushland it is also a common garden bird of town and suburb. The fourth species, the Abert's towhee (*Pipilo aberti*) lives in the dense shrubbery along watercourses of the arid Southwest.

The related olive sparrow (*Arremonops rufivirgata*), found from Mexico to the brushlands of southern Texas, vaguely recalls the green-tailed towhee but is smaller and plainer: olive green above, dull whitish below.

Grassland Sparrows of Distinctive Appearance

Many grassland sparrows are obscurely colored and retiring in habits, difficult to observe and to identify. By contrast, a few have distinctive markings and are easily detected. These include the lark bunting, the lark sparrow, the dickcissel, and the vesper sparrow.

Where the grass was taller on the northern plains I found the lark buntings (*Calamospiza melanocorys*), 6 inches long, conspicuous in mid-summer. They nested in loose colonies and the showy males, black with conspicuous white wing patches, sang from the taller grass stems or flew twenty or thirty feet in the air and then on widespread fluttering wings gave their loud, rich flight song. Already other males were moulting into the streaked brown female-like dress in which they would winter, perhaps as far south as Mexico.

The lark sparrow (*Chondestes grammacus*) is one of the many streaked sparrows of the grasslands, but with two striking differences. The male, singing from a fence post, weed stem, brush or treetop, shows a head pattern of rufous, white and black; it has a black spot on the middle of its plain gray breast that makes recognition easy, and its song ranks near the top among sparrow songs. The writing of old-time naturalists is generally overly emotional but part of Robert Ridgway's description of this bird's song merits repeating—"a series of chants, rich, low and clear, interrupted with emotional trills—a gush of sprightly music, now gay, now melodious, then tender." Ranging over many of the central and western grassland states, the lark sparrow has profited by agriculture to increase its range.

Top: *Dickcissel* (*Spiza americana*)
Bottom: *Slate-colored junco* (*Junco hyemalis*)

A male dickcissel (*Spiza americana*) perched on a weed stalk singing "see see dick, dick-cissel cissel," is a familiar sight in the bird's headquarters in meadows and croplands of the Midwest. But the first one I saw was a wanderer that came aboard a ship in the Bay of Fundy. During my years near Chicago I saw but three colonies, all small. Two lasted for only a year. The third got a good start in an old field, the half dozen males, true to form, singing from weed stalks and periodically chasing females that presumably had nests in the tangled lower weeds and grass. But on my next visit I found the field plowed for corn and the birds gone. This illustrates the erratic occurrence and wandering of this bird that once nested east to New Jersey, and whose colonies seem to change frequently, with or without man's interference. The female dickcissel, 6 inches long, is a sparrowy streaked bird, but the male has distinctive rufous shoulder patches, a yellow breast and a black patch across the throat. In winter when the birds migrate to the tropics, the males are more like the females.

The vesper sparrow (*Pooecetes gramineus*) recalls both eastern dusty country roads and fields where they often associate with tree sparrows, bathe, as well as sing from fence posts, and also the northern short-grass prairies where they share the heavily grazed open range with longspurs and horned larks. Although basically a streaked grassland sparrow, the vesper sparrow has two distinctive marks: white outer tail feathers, conspicuous in flight, and a rufous patch on the bend of each wing. It is different too in its very pleasing song, in being easy to see, and in gathering in small flocks in winter as it moves south.

Streaked Grassland Sparrows

It takes an advanced, enthusiastic bird student to appreciate the six species of sparrows grouped here. They are nondescript, secretive, and hard to see, without conspicuous field characters, and without distinctive songs. All are small, 5-6 inches long, with upperparts streaked brown, black and grayish and with underparts that show dark streaks on the breast, except for one species which is plain buffy. They live in grasslands, run mouselike when disturbed, and are best seen when the males perch on tall grass stems, low branches or fences to sing their insect-like songs. All northern birds move to southern states or Mexico for the winter.

The savannah sparrow (*Passerculus sandwichensis*) is the most common and widespread species, from hayfields of the East, to the more grassy plains and prairies, the salt marshes of California, and the mountain and arctic tundra. It is also less retiring than the other species, and driving along country roads one sees them running on the ground and perched on fences singing. The slightly larger Ipswich sparrow (*Passerculus princeps*) is the savannah sparrows's counterpart, breeding only on the tiny Sable Island off Nova Scotia and wintering along the Atlantic coast.

The other four species are smaller and more retiring. The Baird's sparrow (*Ammodramus bairdii*) of the northern edge of the prairies, the Le Conte's sparrow (*Passerherbulus caudacutus*) also of the northern plains, and the Henslow's sparrow (*Passerherbulus henslowii*) of the Great Lakes area eastward to the Atlantic, all have streaked breasts. The last species, the grasshopper sparrow (*Ammodramus savannarum*), breeding across the northern half of the country, differs from the above in having an unstreaked, buffy breast.

Salt Marsh Sparrows

The only song birds living in the tidewater salt marshes of the Atlantic coast are the three seaside sparrows and the sharptailed sparrow, which also has a population in the marshes of the northern prairies. These birds are similar to the streaked grassland sparrow of the preceding sections in general appearance and behavior; streaked small birds living their unobtrusive lives mostly within the grass and other sheltering vegetation. However, the sizzling or sputtering songs delivered from a tall grass stem are a characteristic summer song of the marshes and these birds also fly up a few feet into the air to utter their husky "tischee;" I remember this last as a characteristic feature of the Bay of Fundy coastal marshes. The more northern sharp-tailed sparrow (*Ammospiza caudacuta*) has a gray cheek patch outlined with bright ochraceous lines; the more southern seaside sparrow (*Ammospiza maritima*), dusky seaside sparrow (*Ammospiza nigrescens*) and Cape seaside sparrow (*Ammospiza mirabilis*) which replace each other geographically, are much duller, brown and grayish.

Bachman's Sparrow and its Relatives

The five small, ground-living sparrows grouped here are among the least known. They are a southern group. In a way they take the place of the more northern streaked grassland sparrows, though none have streaked breasts. Those that live in the arid, more open grass, brush and cactus vegetation of the Southwest are, on this account, easier to see than the secretive birds of the better watered, more densely grassed areas.

The Bachman's sparrow (*Aimophila aestivalis*) lives in the grass and weedy growth of open stands of pine and oak from the southern Midwest to Florida and Texas. One would be as likely to notice a mouse as this bird were it not for the clear whistle and trill of its song. The related Botteri's sparrow (*Aimophila botterii*) lives in the taller grass of the southwestern plains. The Cassin's sparrow (*Aimophila cassinii*) lives only in the southwestern desert shrub and cactus country. The rufous-winged sparrow (*Aimophila ruficeps*) is a bird of grassy tussock of the southwestern mountain slopes and canyons.

Black-throated and Sage Sparrows

Active even during the hottest midday hours when most desert animals seek shade and rest, the stylish black-throated sparrow (*Amphispiza bilineata*) runs over the open sand, gravel, and rocks among the desert shrubs picking up fallen seeds, gleans through the shrubs for a few insects and mounts to the top of a bush to utter its tinkling song. In summer it may live where there is no drinking water, supplying its bodily needs from its insect food, and perhaps cactus fruits. This enables it to live in the hottest and dryest parts of the arid Southwest. It has a black face, chin and throat with a white eyebrow line and mustache streak; otherwise it is gray above, white below. The related sage sparrow (*Amphispiza belli*) is also a bird of the arid southwestern shrubbery, especially sage and chaparral.

Juncos

Unlike many of the related sparrows, the adult junco, 5-6 ½ inches long and gray and white, or gray, brown and white, is not streaked. The flashing white outertail feathers are its first recognition mark. As breeding birds they replace each other geographically, but in their more southern winter quarters several may be found in one area.

When autumn leaves begin to fall in the farming country, the slate-colored junco (*Junco hyemalis*) arrives from the north. All winter small flocks visit lawns and yards for bird seed, and roam the weedy edges of country roads and fields where they often associate with tree sparrows. They delay their spring departure until late, and each spring we hear their trilled mating song from a conspicuous perch, the same song heard in their nesting grounds, on the edges and in clearings of the northern coniferous forests across the continent. This slate-colored bird, with pink bill, white belly and white outertail feathers is one of the easiest of small birds to identify.

The related Oregon junco (*Junco oreganus*) nesting in the western mountains is the counterpart of the slate-colored, but has a red brown back and flanks. The white-winged junco (*Junco aikeni*), nests in the Black Hills area of the Dakotas and the gray-headed junco (*Junco caniceps*) in the central Rockies. The Mexican junco (*Junco phaeonotus*), lives in the mountains of Arizona and Mexico.

Chipping Sparrow and Relatives

If one is tired of trying to watch and identify the nondescript secretive streaked sparrows that run like mice in the grass, the chipping sparrow (*Spizella passerina*) and its relatives, about 4-5 inches long, come as pleasant experiences. They feed in the open, perch on shrubs and branches, go in flocks in the non-breeding season, and are easy to detect. No sparrow merits the name "dooryard bird" more than does the chipping sparrow. Besides living in forest edges and clearings across the continent, it hops about on lawns and dooryards and perches in trees and shrubbery of the country and town. It is easy to identify too: streaked back, gray underparts and with diagnostic solid rufous crown and a black line through the eye.

When winter sweeps across the northern states it brings the tree sparrow (*Spizella arborea*) from the edge of the Arctic. Flocks of these birds forage through the stands of weeds and grass projecting through the snow and hop about searching for fallen seeds. Their voice, an icy tinkle, fits in with the snowy scenery glittering in the sunshine. It looks somewhat like the chipping sparrow but with a less distinct face pattern; the final clue is a dark spot in the center of the gray breast.

Unlike the chipping sparrow, the related field sparrow (*Spizella pusilla*) stays in the fields overgrown with weeds or bushes and in overgrown pastures. It lives on the edges of villages, but not in them. It is much like the chipping sparrow, but its crown and back are both streaked, its bill is conspicuously pink, and the whole face, almost without pattern, gives the bird a blank or innocent expression. Many people recognize its song before seeing the bird, a pleasing sequence of sweet notes that quicken to a trill.

Other relatives are: the clay-colored sparrow (*Spizella pallida*) of the brushlands of the northern prairies; the Brewer's sparrow (*Spizella breweri*) of the more arid sagebrush to the west and the shrubbery above timberline in the northern Rocky Mountains; the little known black-chinned sparrow (*Spizella atrogularis*) of the mountain slopes and tablelands of the Southwest where stands of shrubbery are interrupted with rock outcrops and scattered pines and junipers; and the Worthington sparrow (*Spizella wortheni*) of Mexico which is of doubtful status in New Mexico and Arizona.

Crowned Sparrows

The four handsome crowned sparrows, the white-throated, the white-crowned, the golden-crowned and the Harris' have adults with conspicuous head markings. They are 6-8 inches long, with streaked brown backs and breast and belly with little or no streaking. Their summer homes are on the Arctic tundra and in clearings, shrubbery, and glades in the coniferous forests of the North and of the western states, and all of them winter southward within our limits.

The white-throated sparrow (*Zonotrichia albicollis*) has engaging qualities that make it a favorite, familiar bird. It is relatively tame and common, easily seen, and easily recognized by sight and by ear. The sweet, plaintive song, according to New Englanders, says, "Poor Sam Peabody Peabody," while Canadians claim it says, "Oh Sweet Canada Canada." The white-throat nests in what many people know as the vacation land of the north woods, the spruce-pine forests, from New England to Lake Superior and Mackenzie. In migrating to southern states it often appears on lawns and village greens and its song is heard on both spring and autumn passage. Its markings are a narrow white crown stripe, white eyebrow stripe, and a white throat patch.

In the West the white-crowned sparrow (*Zonotrichia leucophrys*) nests from the Arctic south to California, from 12,000 feet to sea level, and their summer homes have profited by the way man has altered the landscape for farming and pasture, giving them bare ground on which to forage, and shrubbery into which to retreat for safety. In parts of the West in winter the large flocks feed along roadsides and in city parks. East of Alaska, the species nests only in the northern barrens and in settled areas is only a winter visitor or bird of passage.

The other two crowned sparrows are the golden-crowned sparrow

(*Zonotrichia atricapilla*) nesting in Alaska and the northern Rocky Mountains above timberline, and the Harris' sparrow (*Zonotrichia querula*), which nests in the central Canadian Arctic but winters in Oklahoma.

Song Sparrow and its Relatives

The song sparrow (*Melospiza melodia*) group also includes the Lincoln, swamp and fox sparrows. They are from 5 to 8 inches long; all have streaked backs, favor shrubbery as a place to live, feed mostly on the ground, and tend to be northern in distribution, with partial migration southward in winter.

In my youth I was told that the song sparrow's song, first heard when the snow was melting, said "hip hip hurray boys spring is here," and I continue to fit its variable song into this phrase. Its cheerful persistent singing and its tolerance for human habitation, as well as hedgerows, farmland, pastures, brushland, and forest edge over much of the continent, makes the song sparrow well liked and well known even though the main distinguishing mark in its sober plumage is the dark spot in the middle of its streaked breast.

The related Lincoln's sparrow (*Melospiza lincolnii*) of more restricted range in the North and in the western mountains is of a more retiring disposition. The swamp sparrow (*Melospiza georgiana*) of swamp, marshes, bogs and shrubbery along the edges of streams is too retiring to be well known and breeds only in the northeastern and north central United States and northward.

White-throated sparrow (*Zonotrichia albicollis*)